THE NORDIC TRANSLATION SERIES

Sponsored by the Nordic Council
of the governments of Denmark, Finland,
Iceland, Norway, and Sweden

PUBLISHED IN
THE NORDIC TRANSLATION SERIES

FROM DENMARK

H. C. Branner, *Two Minutes of Silence*. Selected short stories, translated by Vera Lindholm Vance, with an introduction by Richard B. Vowles. 1966.

Jacob Paludan, *Jørgen Stein*. Translated by Carl Malmberg, with an introduction by P. M. Mitchell. 1966.

FROM FINLAND

Hagar Olsson, *The Woodcarver and Death. Träsnidaren och döden*, translated by George C. Schoolfield. 1965.

Toivo Pekkanen, *My Childhood. Lapsuuteni*, translated by Alan Blair, with an introduction by Thomas Warburton. 1966.

F. E. Sillanpää, *People in the Summer Night. Ihmiset suviyössä*, translated by Alan Blair, with an introduction by Thomas Warburton. 1966.

FROM NORWAY

Aksel Sandemose, *The Werewolf. Varulven*, translated by Gustaf Lannestock, with an introduction by Harald S. Næss. 1966.

FROM SWEDEN

Peder Sjögren, *Bread of Love. Kärlekens bröd*, translated by Richard B. Vowles. 1965.

Karin Boye, *Kallocain*. Translated by Gustaf Lannestock, with an introduction by Richard B. Vowles. 1966.

OTHER TRANSLATIONS TO COME.

My Childhood

LAPSUUTENI

translated from the Finnish
by Alan Blair
with an introduction by
Thomas Warburton

My Childhood

by Toivo Pekkanen

The University of Wisconsin Press
Madison, Milwaukee, and London, 1966

Published by
The University of Wisconsin Press
Madison, Milwaukee, and London

U.S.A.: Box 1379, Madison, Wisconsin 53701
U.K.: 26–28 Hallam Street, London, W. 1

English translation copyright © 1966
by the Regents of the University of Wisconsin

Originally published in 1953 by
Werner Söderström Osakeyhtiö
Helsinki, Finland

Printed in the United States of America
by the Kingsport Press, Inc.

Library of Congress Catalog
Card Number 66–22862

Introduction

In modern Finnish and Scandinavian literature, certain authors have come to be known as "autodidactic writers." Such a term appears to imply that art is normally created by and for educated people only. This is a distinction not made, I believe, in countries where literature and literacy have traditions reaching further back.

Naturally, in any relevant sense, every writer is self-taught; he has to learn for himself how to express what he wants to communicate. Admittedly, this process of learning will probably be easier in its early stages if the writer has had a formal education. On the other hand, such training is likely to influence him simply to conform to established views.

Toivo Pekkanen, however, lived through the singular experience of being an autodidact twice over. The first time he learned how to write by the normal method of reading, reading, and then reading still more. The second time he taught himself to hew his words loose like chips from what must have seemed a mountain of granite darkness. Both times he succeeded in expressing what he sought to express, with few side glances at literary fashions or patterns.

Toivo Pekkanen was born in 1902, the son of a stonecutter in the coastal town of Kotka in the southeast of Finland. As the reader of this book will soon perceive, Pekkanen's family was both poor and uneducated, wholly proletarian in type. At the same time, his was a family of solidity and solidarity, a home where fundamental human values were held in deep respect. It was also a family offering scope and growing space to imagination and emotions. Father Pekkanen was a muser by nature, perhaps a dreamer, scarce of words but often engaged in reflecting on the ways of the world and given to inventing tales and bedtime stories for his son. This rocking-chair philosopher had, not unnaturally, married an extrovert. Toivo Pekkanen's mother is described as sharp and lively, quick of laughter, tongue, and eye, qualities traditionally prominent in people of Carelian origin. In Toivo's early life his father symbolized tales and meditation in the evening dusk, while his mother represented daylight, laughing affection, and practical thought. He grew up to resemble his father.

But there is no need, in a preface to this book, to relate second-hand what *My Childhood* has to tell. In it will be found the best account imaginable of Toivo Pekkanen's childhood environment and of the events that influenced him during his first formative years. From the way he tells his story it is easy to deduce what kind of a man he became: his sincerity is obvious.

Toivo Pekkanen is a youth of sixteen years when this book ends. Only eight or nine years later his first short story was to appear in print. While in primary school he had discovered the joys of reading and he became a frequent visitor at the town library. There he also had the good fortune to find an understanding friend who guided his reading and encouraged his plans of writing.

To support himself, Pekkanen continued his job as a metalworker until 1932. This meant that his early books were conceived and completed in more or less unfavorable circumstances, often at night, with nerves racked and eyes strained. His health was never very good, and his weak constitution was sometimes pushed to the breaking point by overwork. Otherwise, he was an active young man who took an interest in boxing and athletics and for some years served as an official of his local trade union. This span of time, up to his thirtieth year of age, can be regarded as his maturing period, during which he achieved some realization of his potential as a creative artist.

Toivo Pekkanen was one of the first writers to represent a "new" generation of the Finnish working class, which was beginning its long and difficult disengagement from the cruel events of the civil war in 1918. The influence of this war on Finnish politics and social life can hardly be underestimated. The grim fight between Whites and Reds created a deep-running cleft through the nation; for decades afterwards, victors and vanquished maintained their distrust and hatred of each other. It fell to the younger generations to begin the task of bridging this great gap, a task not fully accomplished until rather recently. Those who had been too young to take arms at the time, and those who had objected to the rebellion, saw the need perhaps not always for reconciliation, but at least for not getting stuck in hate. This new working-class generation was no less class-conscious than its elders, but it had learned a tough lesson. There was hardly a single worker's family in Finland that had not had some personal contact with or suffered a personal loss from the civil war and its corollary concentration camps and imprisonings. The revolution had been quenched. It had even been betrayed by the Red leaders' escape to Soviet Russia, or so, at least, it seemed to those that remained at home. It seemed clear that no one would look after the working man if he did not do so himself. A strict matter-of-fact outlook took possession of the young of the twenties. Things were what they were, and any emotionalism about them had better be ruled out.

Such cool detachment was of good use in developing an artist's power of observation. Toivo Pekkanen's work, from the very start, displays all the characteristics of good naturalism: the eye for detail, the rejection of romantic veils, the wish to expose the drab and harsh sides of life. Here lie the foundations of his art; but it has far more to it than mere outer realism. As Hagar Olsson has commented, Pekkanen is also a writer who inspires zest for life, who convinces one indisputably of the value of life and of what used to be called the greatness of man.

With three volumes of stories, Pekkanen qualified as a writer of promise. With his first novel, in 1932, he won renown. This novel, called *Tehtaan varjossa (In the Shadow of the Mills)*, seemed to announce that the Finnish proletariat had found a spokesman from among its ranks, as indeed it had. But critics and other readers were also quick to acclaim Pekkanen as a thinker free from dogmatic working-class prejudices. *Tehtaan varjossa* is centered round a young steel-mill worker; it does discuss various working class views, and it comes out strongly for social justice, not unlike the young Steinbeck of *In Dubious Battle* and *The Grapes of Wrath* a few years later. But it is also the story of the evolution of a soul. Young Samuel Oino in the novel, whom it is not far wrong to regard as the alter ego of Pekkanen himself, puts up a fight for the growth of his mind, his sensibility, his knowledge and imagination. In circumstances such as his, this is a hard fight. While not very successful in life, Samuel is victorious in spirit. He attains what he needs most: the feeling of belonging, of harmony with the forces of life, of living and working in conjunction with the world around him, and of being free from its restricting pettiness.

The success of *Tehtaan varjossa* enabled Pekkanen to give up working in a factory, which was endangering his health, and to make writing his career. Moving to the capital, he undertook some part-time work as a publisher's reader, and in this capacity he had several opportunities to discover and advise younger talents with a background similar to his own —among them Finland's foremost epic narrator today, Väinö Linna.

Pekkanen's writing continued to grow in scope. His next novels can be regarded as sections of a large fresco depicting contemporary life in Finland, as seen from the standpoint of people from the middle and lower classes. *Kauppiaiden lapset (Merchant Children), Isänmaan ranta (The Coast of One's Fatherland)*, and *Ne menneet vuodet (Those Bygone Years)* depict individual lives and fates against the background of the times, often during the years of depression and hardship. The two latter works, with some additions, were later combined in one volume, *Jumalan myllyt (The Mill of God)*. In *Nuorin veli (The Youngest Brother)* Pekkanen painted a broad scene of the countryside, which he knew less intimately than the town workshops and homes. He did this partly as a satirist, in a vein similar to his portrayals of the well-to-do in *Kauppiaiden lapset*: in both cases we find the proletarian and artist expressing his wary distrust in the ways of the "haves." But in general this row of novels—in part, perhaps, a bit ponderously—constitutes a social document of lasting value.

As a writer of short stories, Pekkanen is as talented as he is as a novelist. His stories are too numerous to describe here. They range from straightforward naturalism to Kafkaesque fantasy and are always sparse and economical in their use of words. Among the longer tales, special mention should be made of the moving, harshly tender, love novelette, *Ihmisten kevät* (*The Spring of Human Beings*), written in 1935, which as a psychological tour-de-force was equaled a few years later by a very differently tuned tale of passion, *Musta hurmio* (*Black Ecstasy*). As a playwright, Pekkanen also has some good and psychologically sound work to his credit.

After World War II, Toivo Pekkanen embarked on his greatest enterprise, destined to remain unfinished. In a large part of his writings there had been present a very distinctive background atmosphere drawn from his native town of Kotka. It continued to fascinate him. He now wanted to depict, in a series of novels, this young town from its foundation in the 1870's, through its growth as a sawmill town and shipping port in Finland's first industrial boom, until his own days. It was a grand theme, fully worthy of an author at the height of his maturity. The first two volumes, *Aamuhämärä* (*Dawn*) and *Toverukset* (*Companions*), promised indeed to crown his life work. The first one, in particular, contains a wealth of information about the conditions of the time and place and— even more significant—develops the first and foremost theme of every great novelist: the vagaries of human nature. They belong to the class of epic works based on purely national material that, nonetheless, have even more to say of the world in general.

In 1948, Pekkanen suffered a cerebral stroke that incapacitated him for months and left him with a form of amnesic aphasia. The names of things, of places, and of persons were lost from his memory, or rather were blocked; he could neither remember them nor, at first, repeat them if they were told to him. Fortunately, he understood the nature of his condition and was able to give himself up fully to the struggle

xii

for recovery. So this became the second autodidactic task of his life. Word by word, with the help of his wife, he conquered his language anew. His recovery was marked by abnormal and incoherent loquacity—a most uneasy symptom for a man who had all his life been a sparing talker. But in the end his will power triumphed, and he had his language at his command once more.

Surprisingly soon he was able to take up his literary work again and in a little over a year completed the third part of his Kotka epic, *Voittajat ja voitetut* (*The Victors and the Vanquished*), which had been half-written when he fell ill. How many more novels the cycle would have comprised is not known; possibly he had intended to write two or even three. But now he did not feel up to the task of continuing and instead completed a number of short stories. His mind had taken a turn toward the weird, fantastic, even macabre, a turn with which he did not feel quite at home either. But then he was not able to feel really at home in life ever again after his shattering experience.

A little later, in 1950 or 1951, he began making notes for *My Childhood*, which finally appeared in 1953. It was to be his last great work, and this delving into his earliest memories probably strengthened his foothold in existence. It is the book of a wise, understanding, and clear-sighted man—and I think Maxim Gorki would have forgiven him for borrowing the title.

In 1954, having translated the book into Swedish, I had the honor of meeting Toivo Pekkanen and passing an evening in his company. He was a man of contrasts—rocklike and eager, reserved and open-hearted. Above all, he was good-natured and friendly, but, as he himself confessed, he was a tired man and living under a cloud.

The last book he published, in 1955, was a volume of

poems, his first and only poetry. And not very much later, on May 30, 1957, took place the event which he had described in the closing poem of the book:

One of these mornings, one spring morning
When the sun rises in the sky
I will mount my steed.

. . . .

Only for a moment shall his hoofs thunder over the rooftops,
Only for an instant shall my shadow flash against the skies.
Already I shall be far away, set free.

Thomas Warburton

HELSINKI, FINLAND

xiv

Bibliography

BY TOIVO PEKKANEN

Rautaiset kädet (*Iron Hands*). Porvoo: Söderström, 1927. (Sketches.)

Satama ja meri (*The Harbor and the Sea*). Porvoo: Söderström, 1929. (Short stories.)

Tientekijät (*The Roadbuilders*). Helsinki: Otava, 1930. (Novel.)

Kuolemattomat (*The Immortal Ones*). Porvoo: Söderström, 1931. (Short stories.)

Tehtaan varjossa (*In the Shadow of the Mills*). Porvoo: Söderström, 1932. (Novel.)

Sisarukset (*The Brothers and Sisters*). Porvoo: Söderström, 1933. (Four-act play.)

Kauppiaiden lapset (*Merchant Children*). Porvoo: Söderström, 1934. (Novel.)

Ihmisten kevät (*The Spring of Human Beings*). Porvoo: Söderström, 1935. (Novelette.)

Takaisiin Australiaan: Pessimistinen komedia pulavuosilta (*Back to Australia: A Pessimistic Comedy from the Years of the Depression*). Porvoo: Söderström, 1936. (Play.)

Isänmaan ranta (*The Coast of One's Fatherland*). Porvoo: Söderström, 1937. (Novel.)

Ukkosen tuomio (*Ukkonen's Judgment*). Porvoo: Söderström, 1937. (One-act play.)

Levottomuus (*Restlessness*). Porvoo: Söderström, 1938. (Short stories.)

Musta hurmio (*Black Ecstasy*). Porvoo: Söderström, 1939. (Novelette.)

Ne menneet vuodet (*Those Bygone Years*). Porvoo: Söderström, 1940. (Novel.)

Raja merellä (*Boarder at Sea*). Porvoo: Söderström, 1942. (One-act play.)

Tie Eedeniin (*The Road to Eden*). Porvoo: Söderström, 1942. (Novel.)

Ajan kasvot: Muistoja ja tunnelmia sotavuosilta (*The Face of Time: Memories and Sentiments from the War Years*). Porvoo: Söderström, 1942.

Hämärtyvä horisontti (*Darkening Horizon*). Porvoo: Söderström, 1944. (Novel.)

Elämän ja kuoleman pidot (*The Feast of Life and Death*). Porvoo: Söderström, 1945. (Short stories.)

Jumalan myllyt (*The Mill of God*). Porvoo: Söderström, 1946. (Novel.)

Nuorin veli (*The Youngest Brother*). Porvoo: Söderström, 1946. (Novel.)

Aamuhämärä (*Dawn*). Porvoo: Söderström, 1948. (Novel.)

Toverukset (*Companions*). Porvoo: Söderström, 1948. (Novel.)

Mies ja punapartaiset herrat. Kuusi kertomusta Miehen vaiheista (*The Man and the Red-bearded Gentlemen: Six stories about the Phases of the Man).* Porvoo: Söderström, 1950.

Täyttyneiden toiveiden maa (The Land of the Fulfilled Wishes). Porvoo: Söderström, 1951. (Novel.)

Voittajat ja voitetut (The Victors and the Vanquished). Porvoo: Söderström, 1952. (Novel.)

Lapsuuteni (My Childhood). Porvoo: Söderström, 1953.

Lähtö matkalle (Departure). Porvoo: Söderström, 1955. (Poems.)

Totuuden ja kirkkauden tiellä. Mietekirja lehtiä (On the Road of Truth and Clearness: Leaves of a Book of Reflections). Porvoo: Söderström, 1958.

Pekkanen, Toivo, and Reino Rauanheimo, eds., *Uuno Kailaasta Aila Meriluotoon. Suomalaisten kirjailijain elämäkertoja (From Uuno Kailas to Aila Meriluoto: Biographies of Finnish Writers).* Porvoo: Söderström, 1947.

ABOUT TOIVO PEKKANEN

Kare, Kauko. *Toivo Pekkanen. Kirjailijankuvan piirteitä.* Porvoo: Söderström, 1952.

Koivisto, E-T. "Toivo Pekkasen Kotka-eepoksen todelli-suuspohjasta," *Ankkapurha: Kymenlaakson osakunnan kotiseutujulkaisuja,* III, Gunnar Rosén and Markus Sauri, eds., Kouvola, 1953.

Kupiainen, Unto. *Toivo Pekkanen runoilijana,* Helsinki: Pellervo, 1955.

Olsson, Hagar. "Efter 1918," *Arbetare i natten.* Helsingfors, 1935.

Viljanen, Lauri. "Suomalainen proletaarikirjailija," *Merkkivaloja. Kirjailijoita täällä ja tuolla puolen maailmansodan.* Helsinki: Söderström, 1929.

My Childhood

CHAPTER ONE

I

A child in the house had died. The coffin had been brought into the hall, and, while the parents were somewhere else, the dead child's sister began to play at death. Collecting all the children in the tenement house around her, she led them into the hall, where the coffin was still resting empty, and began the funeral. A hymn was sung and the lid of the coffin was ceremoniously opened. Being the smallest of the living, I was chosen as corpse and lifted into the beautiful, gleaming white coffin.

For a little while I looked about me contentedly, as I had been lowered into a gauzy, misty whiteness. But when I noticed how solemnly the others were gazing at me, finally taking hold of the lid of the coffin to shut me off from the whole world, I suddenly began to scream. I screamed from inconceivable horror. The offended mourners tried to console me, but this only made my cries grow louder, my legs kick, and my arms jerk. After a vain attempt, they lifted me out of the coffin, and I ran home across the landing to Mother's lap, where I went on crying for a long time.

Is this my life's first experience, the memory of which has stayed with me through the decades? I cannot be sure what really happened, but this is how I remember it. Perhaps this was the very day when the perpetual shadow was cast over me which has never for an instant let me see light alone, but is always there to remind me that every day is followed by night, that every joy is haunted by grief.

My next memory is more pleasant. There was another boy of my age in our house, and one day we went off together on our own. We went out through the front door holding each other tightly by the hand. Before us stretched a small, unpaved street, which led straight to the paved road and the lofty church of the little town. We wandered along in the warm sunshine, rejoicing in the solemn beauty of the world. But the nearer we came to the church, the less we were aware of it. The contours of the big building seemed to dissolve into a huge mass. The high tower vanished from our sight; the wide walls, the tall windows, and the great doors melted away in some way beyond our understanding. And so the church was forgotten.

The church was on high ground and we looked out on many new things. We saw several big buildings and above all we saw the sea.

What was the sea? I myself knew nothing of it, as my father was a stonecutter, but my playmate's father and mother worked on the docks, so he knew a lot about the sea. He had heard the names of ships; he knew the speed of boats and the joyful sound of sails.

"Let's go to the harbor," he said suddenly.

So off we went.

The road led down from the church past houses. We walked along the side of a steep rock which gradually became a high wall. Then we were on a level with the water. We saw the railway lines straight in front of us and beyond them the sea.

A long wharf, about four feet high, had been built of thick logs along the shore. The water that came from far away seemed to run along the surface by the steep wall and sink into the depths. There were boats both moored to the wharf and moving about on the water, near and far. We saw the flash of white sails bellying in the wind. We saw two black steamships which roared threateningly, letting out their hoarse cries fiercely so that people would hear. And besides these we saw, farther out, the ocean-going liners.

What wonderful things to look at! What joy!

We ran across the railway line straight to the wharf, waving our arms and shouting. We explored to right and left, we chattered about what we had seen, we wondered aloud about a hundred unfamiliar things. And when we were tired we sat down on the edge of the wharf and let our bare legs dangle in the air above the deep water beneath us.

One or two seamen and workmen close by remarked, "That's a dangerous spot for those boys. If they fall, they'll drown."

But no one took hold of us. We went on sitting there for hours. And how lovely it was! The warmth of the sun from above and the coolness of the water from below blended delightfully in our bodies. It was good just to exist, but that was not the most important thing. Most important was what we saw—the harbor, endless swarms of boats and big ships, all the colors and sounds of the sea and the harbor. We were spellbound from the very first and held from hour to hour in sweet captivity.

All this time my mother and my playmate's sister, whose duty it was to look after us, were shedding tears of grief and despair. At first they ran round the yard of the tenement house where we lived, asking everyone they met about us, making their way into every room, every shed and outhouse, every attic. As there was not a trace of us, they ran out into the street and into neighboring yards. They worried everyone they met with their questioning. At last they got hold of the police. All in vain. We had vanished utterly.

My mother cried, but my playmate's sister gritted her teeth and said that they must look for us farther afield, all over the town. Mother took one half of the town and the girl the other. Among other places, Mother was to go to the police station to report our disappearance, and the girl was to run right down to the harbor.

This girl, the family's eldest child, was about twelve or thirteen. While the father and mother were at work, the girl looked after her brothers and sisters. Because of this training, she was composed and determined. For that reason she found us.

She found us as evening was drawing on, in the same place where we had settled down in the middle of the day. In the light, warm summer's evening, when people were returning from their work on the big ships far out, there was more for us to see than ever before. The stream of workers, men and women, made us shout with joy. There came one big boatload of them after the other, and their voices were loud and frightening. Such a sight went straight to our hearts, made us tremble and exult, cry and laugh from some quite unknown and incomprehensible cause. It was as if we each had suddenly changed into someone else.

Then we were each seized by a hand and pulled away from the edge of the wharf, two or three yards away from the seething water.

6

Only when our amazement faded did we recognize my playmate's sister, who was standing in front of us deathly pale. She gasped out, "How could you go to such a place! Thank God I have saved you from drowning!"

As we scrambled to our feet she grew really angry. Brushing the dust off our trousers she ordered sharply, "Go home at once!"

As the sights of the harbor vanished from our eyes, we were overcome by weariness, such great weariness that we could have climbed into our mothers' laps and cried ourselves to sleep. But, instead of our mothers, my playmate's sister was in charge of us. She drove us on, sometimes almost at a run. Our crying did not help in the least. Step by step we had to trudge along the strange road. When we tried to stop, she pushed us ahead. On, on, faster, faster!

And what a long road it was! I cannot tell how we got home at last. It seemed to be our life's first road of suffering and pain.

But at last we were home, in the arms of our sobbing mothers. Not only my mother cried, but my playmate's mother, just home from work, cried too. We who had been rescued cried as well, and even our great big fathers almost cried, though they hid their emotion and merely growled. Only my playmate's sister was silent, for she had been forgotten and she grew envious.

For was it not unfair that joy was our lot and she was forgotten, though she was the very one to save us?

My third memory from my very early days was something which I think happened the following year, as I already had a real stonebreaking hammer like Father's which Father had got for me. The owner of the tenement house had had long, heavy stones brought to both sides of the corner house. These stones, cut straight, were to separate the footpath from the road where the horses were driven. But it was a long time before the work was completed. The stones were merely a reminder of how the street would one day be. Or perhaps the town council was still unable to decide how high or low the stones were to be placed. All that mattered to me was that they had been brought there just when Father had given me a new stonehammer.

It was a fine, warm summer. As yet there was no ugly autumn, cold winter, or wet spring in my life. There were not even rainy or windy summer days. There was always warmth and sunshine. Father went off to work so early in the morning that I never saw him go. Mother was the only one at home when I woke up. She would dress me and feed me and then take me outside. For some reason I met no other children at all at that time; I would just go with my mother as far as the street. Mother, basket in hand, would then walk on out of sight to get food from the market, but I would remain at the gateway beside the stones. I would sit down and begin chipping at the stones with my hammer and soon forgot everything else. I forgot friends and strangers, I forgot the passersby and the big draft horses, I forgot Father and even Mother. I sat there cutting at a stone, cutting so hard that I made the dust rise and the stone crack slightly. There were tiny pits on the even surface of the stone and I felt I could be proud of my work.

So it happened on many a morning, probably during many a week. The buying of food may not have been as easy then as it is nowadays; the day's dinner had to be chosen from among wagonloads and stalls in the marketplace. There were so many different things that it made you feel quite giddy at the sight of them. For this reason Mother was sometimes away for several hours, but she would always come home almost running, with her basket brimming over. Then I would leave my work and examine what was in the basket. Cakes were what I

8

specially looked for, and there were always so many that I had no appetite left for proper food, much to Mother's annoyance.

"I won't bring any cakes tomorrow," she would threaten sternly.

But I knew quite well that life would go on tomorrow just as it did today, for as long as I wanted. Mother could not come home from the market without bringing something I liked.

On the contrary, it was I, not Mother, who caused a big upset in our life. One day I stopped chipping my stone for some reason and began to look about me, just as though I expected something to appear. And suddenly a man passed near me pushing a heavy load of tools that had just been sharpened in the stonemasons' workshop. I stood up at once and threw my hammer over my shoulder. I knew those strange tools, although I had never seen them at close quarters. And they seemed to beckon me to go with them.

Quiet as a mouse, with my hammer on my shoulder, I followed the load of heavy tools. I did not dare to speak to the man, but kept behind him. We went for some distance along the same road where I had walked long ago with my playmate to the church and from there to the harbor. But now we stopped before we got to the church, so we were quite near home. A high fence had been built almost in the middle of the road, and from inside it came the sound of lively voices. The wide gate was open and the man disappeared inside with his load. I stared at it for perhaps a minute before I dared to follow him.

Where was I? I saw the foundation of a large building being blasted. I heard countless noises—the protest of splitting rock, the howl of steel, the creak of carts, the shouting of men. A thick dust filled the air, dust from the ground and the shattered rock.

At first no one noticed me, so that I could marvel in peace at the stupefying sight and by degrees calm down a little.

9

Only when a horse came in from the street pulling a heavy load was I forced to move aside into the midst of a group of stonecutters. Then the men noticed me, the men who had the same kind of smock as I had.

"Who's this man?" they asked. "He has brought his hammer. He must be going to break stones!"

And they looked at me in great amusement. One of them asked where I lived, another if my father was a stonecutter. Was my mother at home? I began to enjoy myself and answered readily. I told them where I lived, where Mother was, and I particularly told them that Father was a stonecutter and that I was going to be one too. To tell the truth, I actually boasted of my skill at stonecutting.

The men were still more amused and laughed out loud— hah, hah, haa, heh, heh, hee, hoh, hoh, hoo—each in its own way.

"He's a man all right," they said approvingly. "He'll make a good stonecutter."

And I was put to work with my hammer beside a large rock that had been blasted out of the ground. I was not daunted, but struck my hammer into its rough flank. I struck once, twice, ten, a hundred times, and the dust from the rock surface rose into the air like a cloud.

"Good, good," the men laughed. "Good, good! Go on, go on, boy!"

And I went on eagerly, even after the men started their own work. It seemed natural to me that each one hewed his own stone. Only when my arm grew tired did I begin to watch the men's work more closely. They were using larger tools of all kinds, but I did not mind. I noticed that in their hands the big stones were broken up quickly. I did not quite understand what they did to the stones, but what I saw made me set to work again and again on my big rock.

But unfortunately I did not get very far with my work, simply because my strength gave out. At last all I could do was to watch the others' work more closely, and a feeling crept into my mind that I was nowhere near as good as they were. Only then did I notice a man who was not hewing stones but was carrying stone chips and sandlike dust in two buckets which he emptied into a heap by the side of the road.

I watched this man for a long time as he walked to and fro with his load. I noticed that the man was older than the others and that he was tired, silent, and unassuming. I realized that his work was more humble than the stonecutters', but nevertheless I took a fancy to it and to him.

"Hey, mister," I said to the stonecutter nearest to me, "even if I can't cut stones as you do, I can carry sand and little stones!"

The man glanced at me and burst out laughing. "Hah, hah, haa, hoh, hoh, hoo, that's a good one. But have a try."

As the carrier got near, the man told him to stop and put the buckets down on the ground.

"Go on, you take them the rest of the way," he said to me with a guffaw.

I took hold of both buckets at once, one in one hand, one in the other. I exerted all my strength to lift the buckets and carry their contents to the heap. But to my amazement I could not budge them. Not even enough for them to make a tiny sound. Although I mustered my strength many times so violently that my neck hurt and I was half blinded, they did not budge. It felt as if they were rooted to the ground.

The men roared with laughter—hah, hah, haa, heh, heh, hee, hih, hih, hee. Some had to hold their sides, their mirth was so great. Others grew quite hoarse from laughing.

All except the old man, the carrier. He did not laugh; he just felt rather sorry for me.

11

In my rage I let go of one of the buckets and grabbed the other with both hands. But even that was no good. I was not strong enough to move even one bucket.

Only by degrees did I realize that I was too small to do a man's work. I felt a deep and bitter disappointment. My whole picture of life was shattered and I could find nothing to replace it.

The old man carried the buckets to the heap and the men returned to their work.

I too went back to my stone, but I did not hew it. I probably tried to think of something. I cannot remember where my thoughts led me, but for a long time they kept me dejected and silent. I did not even answer the eager questions and continuous joking of the men. I looked past them at the old man.

At last it was lunch time. All work stopped. Everything fell silent. Some of the men went away, probably to eat at home, but most of them picked up their birchbark haversacks or bundles, looked for a comfortable place to sit, and took out their lunch. And as soon as they began to eat, they thought more seriously of me than before.

"You must go home to lunch," they said. "Your mother will be wondering where you've gone."

A young man took my hand and promised to put me on the way. But when we got to the gate and he asked which way we were to go, I could not tell him. Everything I saw seemed unfamiliar. I could not say whether we lived near at hand or far away, to the right or left, on this street or some other. My companion, not knowing where to take me, grew anxious.

"Can't you remember at all which way you came?" he asked.

I could not say. Everything seemed strange.

What was to be done with me now? One by one all the others joined in the conversation, but nobody could suggest anything. They did not know where to take me. At last it was decided to let me stay where I was until someone came to look for me.

"I've got some food for you," shouted one of the men. "Come over here."

"So have I," called a second, third, and fourth.

The young man took me back to the group of men and collected butter and bread, pork and mutton, milk and buttermilk. Then I was set down in a comfortable spot and the food was pushed into my hands.

"Eat now," my guardian said, "eat all you can."

And I ate. Never did food taste as good as it did then. I ate until my stomach was quite round and in so doing forgot all my sorrows, even that I was a worse workman than the others. I began once more to take part in the general talk and boast in the same way as when I first came.

So the lunch hour passed. But when the men went back to work, I began to feel sleepy. Try as I would to work with my hammer at my big stone, nothing came of it. My blows got slower and slower, my head jerked down onto my chest, my eyes closed, the hammer fell to the ground, and at last I stretched out full length and forgot the whole world.

When the men noticed what had happened to me, one of them came up and lifted me into a better place out of the sun where the ground was softer under my body.

How long did I sleep? Perhaps an hour, perhaps two, perhaps longer.

When I awoke, a strange man was standing in front of me. But at least I knew his dress, the spurs of his boots, his saber, and his sharp-pointed, frightening helmet. Almost from birth, everyone knew the police and felt the stern and awful side of life draw near when they came in sight. So I too started up, trembling for some vague reason. But to my amazement the policeman smiled in a very kind way and said, "Heh, heh, we're awake, we're awake. Let's go home now to Mother. That's the best place to be."

He took me by the hand and told the men that my mother had been running round the town for hours and had then gone to the police station to ask the police to look for her son. And of course they had searched high and low for me, even in the sea.

"And now we've got him, heh heh, hee, though you meant to steal him for yourselves."

As he said this, the policeman looked at the men, hoping that they too would laugh at his joke. But the men muttered something inaudible and went on working harder than ever. They seemed to have forgotten me altogether. Their work absorbed them completely.

The policeman waited for a moment, biting his lips. Then his face flushed and he set me moving with a violent push. When I cried out in distress that my hammer was left behind, he went back to where I had slept, picked up the hammer, and, still more violently, pushed me into a run.

Not until we were in the street did he calm down a little and look at me kindly again. "Won't it be nice to get back to Mother?" he asked. "Won't it?"

"Yes," I answered, not frightened of him a bit. I almost began to admire his uniform, especially his large, flashing saber.

When we got home, I saw Mother running down the stairs with her hair flying, sobbing with joy. She threw her arms round me and squeezed me to her breast so hard that it hurt, while kisses and tears rained on my face, chest, and hands.

"I got you back again, I got you back, I got you back, you naughty runaway. Darling, darling boy, naughty bad boy."

"Heh, heh, hee," laughed the policeman beside us. "Heh, heh, hee. Even we do some good sometimes, don't you think so, lady?"

Only then did Mother recognize the policeman as a policeman. She broke off suddenly and expressed her thanks silently in a deep curtsy. She curtsied deeply over and over again without saying a word.

"Heh, heh, hee," the policeman went on, laughing for some time, boasting how he had found me on the working site of a big new building. But gradually he had to stop laughing and at last even talking. He had to stop praising himself to Mother, because Mother gave him not one word in answer, though it was she who had run to the police station and made them go and look for me.

"Goodbye," the policeman said at last rather sharply. "Goodbye."

He saluted and walked away. Mother curtsied once more, but said nothing. In a world ruled by the Russian Emperor, the police commanded respect, but one could not love them. I again had the strange feeling that the policeman had aroused, though now and then I had actually liked him.

II

Such are my earliest memories. Not until later did a picture form in my mind of my home and of Mother and Father.

Mother was much livelier than Father. She laughed very often and a song was nearly always pouring from between her red lips. Her cheeks too were red and her hair was dark and very thick. Her figure was inclined to be round and stout, but she was as light as air. She never kept still, not even at her work, but flitted to and fro all the time for no reason.

Father I saw much less often than Mother, but for all that he was more exciting than Mother. When he got home from work, he would wash his hands and face, sit down at the table, quickly swallow the food Mother gave him, and move over to the rocking chair. That was where he rested, and once there he seemed to rock away from everyday life. Mother neither knew nor understood anything of this. His silence only got on her nerves. But I knew and understood, I who clambered up into his lap every evening.

Where did we really go to? Somewhere very far away, where Mother's chatter was not heard, where quite different sounds and sights were to be heard and seen. It was very quiet and beautiful there, with only the soft murmur of delightful sounds.

There, far away, Father would talk to me. He told me of his work as a stonecutter and promised that I too would become a stonecutter. He told me of his past, of his childhood in the country, of his coming to this town where we now had our home, and of the future, when he would be old and I grown-up. And last of all he would tell me of those things which are not of this world, but are beyond the earth and the visible sky, farther than the North Star and the moon and the sun, with God and the angels. Of that which we all reach at last.

I heard of many things which Mother did not even know existed.

Sometimes I woke up to find that I was being undressed and put to bed. I heard Mother's voice again quite clearly and saw Father take the water and the slop pail and go outside. Mother had asked him to fetch water and empty the dirty water away. But more often than not I fell asleep without this scene in which Father played the servant, and I would not see him again until the following evening, when he took me once more on to his lap.

Mother I saw all day long, from morning to evening, except when she went marketing in the mornings. Mother dressed me, fed and washed me, took me out and brought me in. Mother talked to me aloud, kissed me, sang all kinds of songs to me, took me in her arms a thousand times a day, cried

16

when I was out of her sight. I loved her dearly. But with her we were merely on the bright sunny earth. Everything round us was plain and obvious. That is why I always left her as soon as it was evening and Father came home. I would rush into his arms, and he took me far away, to secret lands and skies.

Not even now can I explain how Father took me with him on the journeys of his mind. Only during those short moments when Mother was not at home would he hum to me a song about a star, the North Star. But as soon as Mother came back, he was silent. And all that mattered to me was this secret silence of his, the journey to far away.

III

The house was a tenement house. We came out of our room first into a dark hall, which we shared with our neighbor and which led to some steep stairs. At least I thought they were dangerously steep. There were five or six steps, and when I happened to go up or down them without Mother's help, I could only manage by gripping the banisters tightly with both hands.

The yard was of smooth sand or some kind of earth trodden hard. On the other side of the yard were low buildings of various kinds—pigsty, stable, woodshed, outhouses—and the drain and the well. At both ends of the yard were high, broad gates which led to the different streets. I went through either gate just as hopefully, as there were plenty of stones to be broken in front of each of them.

I know nothing more about the yard, because it did not interest me, nor do I remember anything of the other children. Of the people existing outside the house I knew only one at this time—our landlord, who was mayor of the town.

He did not live where we did, but in a better house of his

own somewhere. But he had a shed here, between the out-house and the stable, and when he came to this money-making house of the poor he would always bring something to the shed—an old horseshoe he had picked up in the street, a rusty nail, a bit of metal. He valued metal so highly that he thought it downright folly to leave even a tiny fragment in the street or on a scrap heap. To his way of thinking, metal was the basis of wealth. But as his friends and acquaintances did not fully share his view, the quirk of an old man, he stored his bits of metal in the shed in our yard.

What was he like otherwise? Unfortunately, all I remember about him is that he was a very stern old man and that he had a nasty stick in his hand. If I was in the yard when he arrived, I would run to the nearest hiding place, but at the same time I jeered at him in my mind. I remembered what the others had said about him: That rich old man is mad. Sane people don't collect rusty and broken horseshoes.

Now and again he came into our room of an evening, when Father was sure to have come home from work. That was on rent days, and Father and Mother were expecting him. In me too the tension grew from one moment to the next. I was afraid of something, although Father and Mother assured me that he would not hurt anybody. Perhaps I was afraid because inside there were not such good hiding places as in the yard, where I had laughed at him. The second our door opened and the landlord's figure appeared, I would slip from Father's protective arms and hide behind him or simply under the bed.

It is strange that I fled from our landlord here as well, for he was very polite when he came to see us. He shook hands with Mother and Father, asked how they were, remarked on the fine weather, and would have patted my head if he could. But I ran away from him, and every time he had to stop after a vain attempt and return to Mother and Father. He would stand in front of them rubbing his hands contentedly as

Father took out his purse, dug the required number of marks out of it, and handed the rent solemnly to the landlord. And at the same time Mother would drop him a respectful curtsy. The landlord snatched the money delightedly, counted it quickly, and put it into his purse as he thanked Father and Mother: "Thank you, thank you, my good man. You're just the kind of people I like. I hope that you live in my house to the end of your days. Thank you, thank you, goodbye, goodbye, good night, my good people."

And backing towards the door he would disappear, bowing politely.

IV

What was this room of ours like? Although I have long tried to recollect what the walls and ceiling, floor and window were like, what colors there were, the shape of our furniture, the kind of lamp and stove, I can remember nothing. I cannot picture the bed in which Father and Mother slept or the place where I spent my nights. The rocking chair is the only thing I vaguely recollect, for as I rocked there in Father's arms I experienced all the most wonderful daydreams of this world and the next.

There were two doors. I do not remember what they were like or the color, but I had known for a long time that one led outside and the other into our front room.

Only now do you hear that we had another room, but I did not mention it before because I was never allowed into it. Only very seldom, when Mother was cleaning the room and the lodger was out, could I peep in the door. But only for a second, as Mother always drove me away.

I never remembered the existence of the door until Mother went into the room or the door suddenly opened without warning from time to time from the other side. I knew quite

well that the man who came out was our lodger, the tele-
grapher, but I gave a start every time. I do not know to this
day why the opening of the door scared me, as the man was
very nice to us, including me. He would sit down and talk
cheerfully about something pleasant which I did not understand but which made Mother laugh and almost shout with
joy and Father smile too. They all got on very well together
and Mother would even sing our lodger's praises. But I almost
hated him whenever he was with us. I kept silent, pressing
myself against Father and staring at him. Years later I realized
that he was a more handsome and much younger man than
Father, as young and good-looking as Mother; but when he
lived with us I did not understand such things. The cause of
my dislike was perhaps a certain evening when I awoke from
a dead sleep.

That evening I realized for the first time that the day had
been a Sunday. Father had been at home all day, sitting in his
wonderful rocking chair from morning to evening. Mother
was very restless for some reason. I sensed it from her behav-
ior. She had no work to do, and she had put on a different
dress from the one she wore on other days. She tried now and
then to sit down like Father, but it was not her nature to keep
still. Even now she had to keep moving about. She hummed
and sang and said a dozen times to Father that they ought to
go out somewhere, for a walk along the streets or to the
woods, to the harbor, or to see friends. And towards evening
Mother was more restless than ever; she even talked about
dancing. This was a word I did not understand at that time,
but rocking as I was in Father's arms and journeying to far-off
star lands, it did not occur to me to ask what it meant.

Father understood it all right, but he no more wanted to go
there than anywhere else. Every time Mother asked him to go
out he refused with a scarcely audible grunt. He was tired

after a hard week's work, he was resting, he did not care for people, and did not want to go dancing. And I knew that we would go off together to quite different worlds.

So evening came, I fell asleep, and was lifted up and put to bed. It meant no change for me, I went on dreaming just the same as during the day. My life was still wonderful for many hours yet.

But suddenly it changed. From somewhere outside me a shrill, piercing cry thrust into my sleep and woke me. At first I was quite unable to grasp where the seat of my terror was, what they were doing to Mother, why they had struck her. I sat up in bed with a start, trembling with fear, and only gradually did I take in what I saw.

The sight lasted only a minute, perhaps less. At first I saw Father, or a man like Father, whose face had quite a different look from any I had ever seen, a wild look of anger and pain. He seemed to be about to throw himself at an enemy; his legs were ready to leap, his hands raised to strike. In front of him stood the lodger, he too ready to strike, but at that moment he drew back to protect someone. Mother!

Mother! Right behind the man stood Mother, small and cowering, a cry of terror on her lips. For she was the one to cry out; it was her scream that had woken me.

As I have said, the sight lasted a minute, perhaps not that long. The door opened, Mother and the lodger disappeared, and the door shut again with a slam. With that Mother's cry died away and Father's heavy, speechless groaning gasp filled the air. Perhaps he felt at once the fury of hatred and the shame of disappointment.

Father stood where he was. He seemed turned to stone. But then my petrified being began to stir. Something unknown and frightful forced its way out from inside me. I began to scream, scream louder than ever before, scream so that my whole body shook, and Father gave a start. Striding over to me, he snatched me in his arms and seemed suddenly to have forgotten everything else except me.

"There, there now, my child," he whispered. "Don't be afraid, everything's all right. Sleep, sleep, little one, hushaby, hush."

He walked back and forth on the floor with me in his arms. And gradually his voice and the warmth of his arms soothed me. I calmed down and fell asleep again.

When I awoke in the morning, everything was as before. Father had gone to work and Mother fed and dressed me. Peer at her as I would on the sly, I could see nothing unusual about her. She petted me and hummed and sang as blithely as ever. With the morning light I had a feeling that I had not known any real evil during the night but only dreamt it. Mother had told me before that small children sometimes have bad dreams.

But I was rather uneasy all day and I waited tensely for Father to come home. What would happen when Father and Mother met? Would it be a happy evening as before, a journey in Father's arms far away to an imaginary, unknown land, or would the cries of the night, the terror and pain, be repeated?

The old, happy evening came into our room with Father. I thought that Father and Mother were trying to be nicer to each other than before, but otherwise everything was the same as it always had been for as long as I remembered.

So I never found out whether I had been dreaming or if there really had been a scene during the night between Mother, Father, and the lodger. I soon forgot it, and I do not know what it may have meant to Mother and Father. But for a long time, a very long time, I hated our lodger, hated him for as long as he lived in our front room.

22

I do not actually remember ever being in our second room, but I suppose I must have gone through it at some time with Mother, as I have a mental picture of the stairs leading from this room to the street. And these stairs were much nicer than those leading to the yard. It was an inside staircase with handsomely painted walls. The stairs were covered by a dark, heavy carpet, a strangely soft-looking carpet into which your feet sank deeply. It was rather dark there, but the outside door opened right onto the street.

There were two doors opening onto this staircase from the same tenements that had the back stairs in common. I do not remember ever having seen our neighbors on the back stairs, but on these grand street stairs I saw them several times.

Who were they? In the early days Mother greeted them very amiably, almost respectfully, and in me they aroused a feeling of real festivity because of their gleaming white dresses. They were laundresses, laundresses of white linen. One of them owned the business and the other two were her assistants.

The really strange thing was the whiteness, a bright, radiant whiteness, that surrounded them entirely. Their own dresses, aprons, and caps were white, and the linen they ironed and carried in baskets and in their arms was white. And it seemed to me as though their faces and even their hands radiated a dazzling whiteness, although they were red just like Mother's face and hands. Perhaps it was the joy of life that comes from youth and health, life's beauty and bravery, that shone from within them and made all other colors glow white.

I saw them very seldom, but every time I saw them I felt happy for a long time, I think all day until bedtime. I thought

23

of them as I cut stones in the street, as I ate on Mother's lap, or traveled with Father to unknown, distant lands. The whiteness of the laundresses went with me even on my journey.

But one day this happiness of mine was shattered. I was there to see Mother and the eldest laundress come to blows on the best stairs leading to the street. They shouted, hit each other, and pulled each other by the hair. The younger laundresses tried to come between them and separate them, but they were flung aside weeping and the same happened to me. All we could do was cry and watch the furious course of anger, hear the wild sounds of malice, and see Mother and the white laundress grow ugly and ravaged, tired and old. That was my part and that of the young laundresses in this scene.

At last Mother, gasping with exhaustion, took me inside and the laundresses disappeared behind their door. With them, for all time, went their lovely whiteness. I have never seen it again.

What had happened? Why had Mother and the laundress fought? That evening Father spoke about it to Mother in a stern, solemn voice. They talked for a long time, so long that Mother began to cry and Father lifted me down on to the floor and took Mother in his arms. It was an impressive sight, a moving and dumbfounding sight, but it did not enlighten me as to the cause of the fight. Instead it planted in my mind an entirely new and strange word—socialism.

Not until long afterwards did I hear that word again and understand what it meant. I found out that the laundress was one of the town's most ardent supporters of this new idea. Whether she had come to blows with Mother because of socialism or for some other reason, I do not know. Nor can I say whether Father felt strongly about it, whether he supported it or not. But that is the stormy way in which I became aware of this idea that revolutionized our age.

Do I remember anything else from this period of my life? I have a picture of Father swimming—swimming in the sea far out from the shore.

One Sunday even Father put on his best clothes and went out with Mother and me. In the street we met another married couple, who had no children. Mother and the other woman began walking side by side and the men walked behind them. We went in a direction I did not know at all. I noticed that quite soon the houses disappeared and the woods began and the street changed to a rutty road. We were going outside the town.

A strange, surprising joy suddenly flooded into me, for I had unexpectedly found quite a new world. I came across all kinds of plants that I had never seen before and never even heard of. I came across unfamiliar leaves, flowers, bushes, and thick, mighty trunks of ancient trees reaching to the sky. I found clean sand which looked quite different from the sand in the streets. I found black soil, smooth stones, and the warm surface of rough rock. Almost every moment I found things that were new, completely new. The way seemed like a triumphal procession, so overwhelmingly joyful that when I suddenly caught sight of the sea and the wooded shore, I had to stop. Joy poured over me so violently that I thought I would choke.

We had come to quite a high rock. Father, who up to now had been talking to the other man, came up and lifted me as high as his arms would reach.

"Look," he said with a laugh. "Look carefully at what you see between the trees. Do you see what is sparkling there like gold and silver? That's where we're going to swim."

The road thus far had climbed gently upwards. Now it began to descend between the pines and the going was rougher and warmer than before. When Father put me down, I quelled the flood of joy and started to run. I left Mother and Father behind me and rushed to the beach. But once at the water's edge I was again forced to stop and consider what it really was that I was now meeting. The beach was shallow and the water very warm; the bottom was dark gray and had a nasty smell. When I threw a small stone, it formed the same kind of bubbles on the surface of the water as the rain did on the streets.

"We're not going to stay here on the beach," Father said as he came up. "The sea washes all the filth and decayed stuff into the shallow bed of the bay. Let's go to the point."

We had suddenly lost sight of Mother and the strangers. Father and I walked on by ourselves along a narrow path. We saw a dance floor and a crumbling rampart, and then we came to quite a new kind of sea and beach—a sea that shimmered bright blue and splashed against the rocks, and a beach with huge boulders and such sharp-pointed sand that I felt it pricking the soles of my feet. And an all-pervading murmur filled the air, the heavy, inexplicable sound of the world when it was young.

Father undressed himself and then me. For the first time I saw what he was really like—a tall, broad-shouldered, bald-headed man, bony rather than muscular, with a brown moustache. All at once I liked him more than ever before, I was proud that he was my father and that I was his son. And when he held out his arms to lift me up again, I was so happy that I threw myself into them and shouted with joy.

Or who knows what I really shouted.

"Don't be frightened," Father said gently. "The sea water feels funny at first, but you'll soon get used to it and then you'll be a swimmer."

He put me down between two big rocks extending into the sea, where there was soft, smooth sand. I screamed with terror when the water suddenly reached to my middle and a chill feeling spread through my whole body. But in the same instant my terror changed to joy and pride, and as Father let me go I beat the water wildly with my hands and the spray wet me all over.

That day I had known joy many times in quite a new way, but the most momentous experience was yet to come. Father stood beside me for some time looking at me and smiling at the noise I made, then he told me to stay where I was and be careful not to go where it was too deep while he himself was swimming.

At first I did not understand what he meant. I saw him dive into deep water from the far edge of a rock. The water began to shower around him in white waves and swallow him from sight. But after a moment his head and right shoulder bobbed up two or three yards away. He shouted to me once more to stay quietly where I was. Then he began to swim on his side, splashing the water with both feet, and keeping his head and right shoulder visible as he moved his arms under the water. Only after a moment did I realize that he was moving forward, farther and farther away, along the wide, almost blindingly bright path of the sun.

I stopped splashing and was silent. I could only watch him. I still admired and loved him unspeakably, and only gradually did something else creep into my mind, something unexplainable, obscure, frightening perhaps. Father was moving farther and farther into the embrace of the sea along the path lighted by the sun.

My vague dread increased and I climbed out of the water. There seemed to be no one anywhere near. I was quite alone and I could plainly hear the eternal murmur of the sea and of the pines growing on the shore and the plaintive sigh of the alders. And all the time Father was swimming farther and farther out, his head and shoulder getting smaller and smaller and looking so frail. Suddenly it seemed that he was not only swimming away from me but also that he was ceasing to exist.

At first I called to him softly, then louder and louder. I clambered up onto a boulder; for a moment I saw him better, and called again. But he was out of earshot and did not hear or see me. He kept swimming out, and his head and shoulder became still smaller and more unreal.

What actually happened to me that day? Mother had already vanished from my life and left me to go alone with Father to the beach. And now Father too seemed to be leaving me. I remember only my cry of anguish and that I climbed to the top of the high rock and saw Father disappearing. But then my mind is a blank. Ransack my memory as I will, I have no mental image of how Father came back from his swim.

It seems to me now that part of my father did swim away from me forever, because after that day our relationship changed in some way.

I remember that we came again to the top of the hill from which I had seen the sea glittering gold and silver between the trees. Then we were all together again. The grownups went back to the town in twos just as we had come, but I no longer kept running off by myself. I walked beside Father, holding him tightly by the hand. I was tired and the only thing that mattered to me now was sleep.

I glanced back from the top of the hill, however, and it seemed as if Father was still swimming far out at sea. Although he was walking beside me, he was at the same time swimming out there, farther than I could conceive, to the other side of the sea, to those strange lands which he had always told me about in his silent words. I felt that from now on I would not understand them, even though I were to climb every evening into Father's arms. But I was so weary that this knowledge did not upset me. All I longed for was bed.

28

CHAPTER TWO

I

I cannot say why or how we moved to another house. When I let memories flow into my mind, I see a new house, an uneven, sloping yard partly covered with sparse trees, a sandy street, and on the other side of it a wide stretch of open ground and a cluster of small, old cottages.

But let us begin with my home. We now had the use of two rooms, but we only went into the sitting room on the few occasions when we had visitors. As a rule we lived in the kitchen. There we had our meals, there we slept, washed, dressed, and undressed, and there too was Father's rocking chair.

The special thing about the rooms was their newness and freshness. The floors and ceilings smelled of paint, and the timbered walls, as yet unpapered, smelled of wood and of the tar-impregnated packing stuffed into the cracks between the logs.

It was here that I first became aware of the kind of furniture around me. All I remember of the sitting room, or "best" room, is a wide, reddish-brown bed, which could be pulled out lengthwise, new rugs, new chairs, and a new table, on which was a much heavier and larger lamp than in the kitchen. Perhaps that is all there was. There was a bed in the kitchen too, but it was black and opened at the side. There was also a table at which we had our meals, some worn chairs, a rocking chair, a wooden chest of drawers and on it the water pails. There were long, narrow rag rugs on the floor, but they looked much older than the ones in the best room, and in places the floor itself soon had the paint worn off. Here too were my toys, the stones and bits of wood. On the wall hung Father's and Mother's clothes. And the most important object of all was the food cupboard, with all sorts of good things on the shelves—homemade bread, on which butter was spread, buns, sugar, and sometimes even cakes.

When I went out in the mornings, I had only to go down two or three steps and I was on the ground. For the people who lived on our left it was still easier; they had only one step, as they were at the top of the slope. But the neighbors on our right had to walk down five or six steps before they reached the yard, as the ground there was so low, on the street level.

On the left at the top of the slope was the same kind of outhouse as at the old house, but it was brand new, the color of clean boards. Our part of it was only a tiny privy, to which we went secretly for a little while, closing the door carefully. Our firewood was under the house. We had no pig since Mother and Father didn't like them, but some people kept them, and there were several in the two pigsties. One of these belonged to the two brothers who owned the house, the other to the tenants.

I usually went straight ahead after I came down the steps, and so went in among the trees. The slope rose higher here than by our steps. I was in a little grove, with moss-covered rocks and low-growing shrubs of blueberries and cranberries. When I went on a little farther, I reached the top of a big rock and the highest point of the ridge. I could see the house next door, their level yard and the other side of the ridge, which was very steep. In fact there was something frightening about it; the smooth rock fell sharply away, there were boulders and piles of stones. There were only a few trees, and they too seemed the worse for their difficult position, their grim struggle for life. Moss grew here and there, but not a single blueberry or cranberry. This strange side of the ridge seemed bare, desolate, and dangerous; I always stopped some distance away to look at it, and only for a little while. A sense of unknown danger forced me to turn away and to forget every time what the other side of the ridge was like.

I would turn to the right, where the ridge sloped gradually down, ending in a brink about ten feet above the street, where the roadmakers at one time had excavated the rocky bed of the ridge. The cutting at this point was even steeper than the side near the next-door house, but it never frightened me. The steepness had been made by people; it was the work of man.

Here at the broken end of the ridge, beside the road, was the foundation of an unfinished house and a lot of building refuse from one that was ready: logs, planks, broken and unbroken bricks, bricklayers' tools, clay, and sand. In the early days, this was my favorite playground. I no longer broke stones, as I had lost my stonehammer. I had taken a fancy to bricklaying and made good use of everything here.

And here I had my first dangerous experience. I don't know what I made the other days, but on that day I was making an oven. I remember quite well. I took bricks from a pile, one after the other, and carried them at a run to a small flat spot by the steep side of the ridge. Each time I laid the brick I had brought in place before going to get another one, and the oven I was making got bigger and bigger. But then something happened. I must have run off from the pile with a large brick in my arms towards my oven, in just the same way as before, but I never got there. Perhaps my feet led me astray, perhaps I forgot my safe path and went another way. At any rate, I suddenly stepped out of the everyday world into unknown darkness.

With the brick in my arms, I stepped off the broken end of the ridge onto the roughly levelled stone surface of the street ten feet or so below. No one saw me, and I plunged into darkness, or rather into sleep, a dreamless sleep in which all awareness of existence vanishes.

How long was it before I came back into our world? Perhaps quite soon. The day was still as fine and sunny as before, and there was not a soul to be seen in the street. The brick I had been carrying lay beside me, its edges battered. My head hurt. Not much, only a little. When I sat up and touched my forehead I felt something funny, and when I looked at my hand, I saw blood. My own dark-red blood, and it had stained my whole hand.

I gave a startled cry, scrambled to my feet, and fled. I ran home. My whole body was shaking and I rushed sobbing into Mother's arms, pressing in as deeply as I could, to get away from that strange power which had drawn me off my safe path.

"What are you crying for, my boy?" Mother said, not understanding my tears and the cause of my flight.

But when she saw the blood on my hand and my bruised head, she consoled me.

"You've fallen and hurt your head," she went on. "Dear, oh dear, you poor wee thing. Mother will bathe your head and bandage it up."

Mother washed my forehead in warm water and then band-

32

aged my head with a strip of clean cloth from one of Father's old shirts. Gradually I calmed down, but I knew I had experienced something very dangerous. For a long time I didn't dare go back to the ridge, but stayed near home or went along the street.

Only now, too, did I get to know the broad meadow on the other side of the street and the cluster of old cottages. In the nearest cottage was a sauna, where I went for my bath with Mother and Father, but all the other cottages were strange to me. When I was alone, I didn't go farther than the gate, even though there seemed to be children in those cottages. I think all the people on our side of the street were frightened of them and spoke ill of them. I did not as a rule play at the gate, but looked and wondered at the big wide world and at all the different things I could see in it—the new and the old houses, the good and the bad people, the town and the woods, the level ground and the high hill just visible in the middle of the woods, much higher even than the hill from which I had seen Father both beside me and swimming far out at sea. No wonder that at the edge of the broad meadow I began to evolve the first thoughts of my own, though as yet they did not become very intelligible.

Later, the following summer, I explored farther afield and found much that was new, but now I always turned back at the gate. There was another spot that I soon became familiar with. My mother's sister and her family lived in the same house. Their steps were much higher than ours, perhaps as high as those we had had in our first home. Having climbed up to the front door, which was in two parts, I opened the right-hand side, went through a dark hall, and opened a second door. I was then in a strange kitchen, which nevertheless I knew quite well from the very first. The mother in it was much fatter and taller than mine and her face was pockmarked. I liked her because she always gave me something good to eat and because her five children were all bigger than me, some of them already the size of grownups.

When I went to see my big, fat aunt in the daytime I would find her alone in the kitchen. She always greeted me cheerfully and sat me down at her big kitchen table.

"Are you hungry, my boy?" she would ask. "Here we are now, have some of this pancake."

And quick as a wink she put something tasty to eat on the table, before I had time to say whether I wanted it or not. This I liked, as my shy nature refused everything when it had to resort to words. Here I had no need to speak at all, but could start eating something good right away. Today a pancake, tomorrow stewed blueberries, the day after tomorrow cranberry pudding, sometimes homemade cake or fancy cakes bought at the shop. We had these at home too, but they were never as good as here.

As I ate all the good things put before me, I would watch my aunt out of the corner of my eye as she bustled about the kitchen. I answered her questions in monosyllables, and hardly gave an ear to her endless chatter. What interested me most, apart from the delicacies, was the speed at which she worked. She cooked large pots of food, darned socks, patched shirts and underpants, ironed the girls' petticoats and dresses, hurried out with the slop pail and brought back a tub of clean water, and fetched firewood in an enormous basket. Everything here was done at a faster rate than at home or anywhere else I knew. That is why I liked it.

And the pace kept getting wilder as the others came home. First came the schoolchildren, a girl several years older than me and a big sturdy boy. They both demanded food at once, biting greedily into the bread and gulping down the milk. They took no notice of me until they had satisfied their hunger. The boy would then start abusing me with a string of stupid gibes, which hurt me. But the girl would at once take

34

my part, stroking my head and praising me, saying what a good little child I was, and so pretty—the nicest and best-behaved little child in the world, and everyone must be kind to me. The boy would laugh scornfully, taunting me with still more impudent words which I could hardly understand and starting to push and poke both me and his sister. Because of me the two schoolchildren would have started quite a fight if the boy had had more time. Fortunately he was in a hurry to get to his own affairs. Having jeered at his sister and me and pushed us roughly, he usually fished out some mysterious objects from under the bed and was out of the door like lightning.

"Oh, he is *horrid,*" the sister said, stamping her foot.

"Now don't say that," her mother said, trying to pacify her. "Boys will be boys. Even your good little boy will be like that when he grows a bit."

But the girl wouldn't hear of this, and began to play with me. I didn't care for this at all. First I was made to sit up in a chair or on the floor, then I was put to bed. I was brushed and combed and dressed in strange clothes; I had this and that pushed into my mouth, but seldom anything nice. Sometimes this schoolgirl, who was only a few years older than I was, snatched me into her arms in a rush of feeling, squeezed me passionately to her breast and whispered in my ear, "You're my own little boy, my very own little boy."

That is how emotional and passionate girls can be. If this game had gone on for long, I would certainly have made my escape. But I knew beforehand that I would soon be set free. As soon as the other schoolgirls had had something to eat in their own homes, three or four of them, sometimes more, rushed in and I was forgotten. The girls played among themselves in another room, where I was not allowed, or went outside.

The crowning point of the family's daily life was in the

35

evening, when the father and two of the older children came home. The eldest boy, dressed in the handsome livery of a coachman, probably didn't come home until much later in the evening, but all the others now gathered round the big table. Auntie lifted the big pot onto the table and filled everyone's plate. Uncle cut the big loaf into slices and spread them thickly with butter. The steam from the hot soup hovered round the whole group. They all began to eat heartily, and only the parents and elder children were allowed to talk. The moment the younger children tried to say anything, Uncle glared at them fiercely, and if that didn't help he started tapping the table with the handle of his sheath-knife. That was enough. The youngest ones grew as quiet as mice. They had a stern father.

This head of the family was particularly interesting be-cause he spoke a funny mixture of Finnish and foreign words. It was he who told me that there were also Swedish-speaking Finns in the world. My mother explained it to me when we got home from our first visit together. Even so, it almost shocked me. Every time he started to speak, I gave a start, and listened with mouth agape to every word he said. It was often difficult to understand them, and it seemed especially odd when he placed our Finnish words in the wrong part of the sentence. On top of everything else, it would have been quite laughable, if one had dared to laugh. But I kept as quiet as possible so that I would not be noticed and so that he would even forget I existed.

Uncle did not seem to bother much about his wife and youngest children. He made the children keep silent, as I said. He expected his wife to wait on him hand and foot, telling her curtly to give him this or give him that, pass this or pass that. The stout, pockmarked woman had to keep an eye out every second in case her husband wanted something, and for this reason she had no time to talk at all. It was the two elder and superior children who did the talking. The boy was a clerk in one of the town's large grocery stores and the girl an apprentice at a milliner's. I've no idea exactly how they were dressed, but it was because of their clothes that they seemed far above the rest of us. This lofty position was further emphasized by their speech, their gestures, the way they wore their hair, everything about them. Their stern father was humble in their presence, taking part in the conversation chiefly by asking questions. He was greedy for knowledge, and the elder children had to feed him with information about everything under the sun. And well informed they were, too. The boy, in particular, seemed to know everything about the past and the present, about our country and the world in general. No matter what their father asked, they had glib answers and were ready with all kinds of explanations, sometimes even in Swedish, as apparently they could not explain the matter sufficiently clearly in Finnish. At one time these two favorite children had gone to a Swedish-speaking elementary school, though they preferred to speak Finnish. Swedish was essential to them in their work. At that time a select grocer's and a fashionable milliner's were patronized only by the Swedish-speaking upper class.

For me, these conversations were the crowning point of my visit. As I was usually forgotten entirely, I was free to listen carefully to every word and to snap up many crumbs of new knowledge. Though I by no means understood everything, not even the meaning of all the Finnish words, I could feel my mental self beginning to grow. In fact I was now vaguely aware that some kind of spiritual ego dwelt inside me. What this part of me was like, or what it represented, I could not say, but it was at least as greedy for knowledge as the spirit of this family's father.

So much for our new home and its surroundings. To me the most important thing about it was that, from the very beginning, it taught me to take a much broader view of the world than before.

II

An historical happening confirms that I was then three years old. That autumn a general strike broke out in Finland. My memories of it are very dim. I heard rumors and at home too it was said that the town councilors and the leaders of the new labor party had met and made an agreement to fight against the Tsar. The event had caused such a stir that Mother and Father sat discussing it until late into the night, and next morning and on the days that followed Father put on his Sunday best and went someplace other than to work for several hours every day.

That is all I remember of this important event. And I had not yet come to know autumn either, though it did me harm and confined me to bed for a long time, just when I first heard Christmas spoken of.

My illness, of course, was measles. Most children have to go through it, perhaps in order to learn that life can be cruel as well as kind. I lay in the wide bed in the kitchen, breathing heavily and feeling thoroughly miserable. I probably had a high temperature. Mother would come over to me now and then to stroke my damp hair and say nicer things to me than ever before. From her I heard about Christmas. I didn't understand just what was meant by the word, but I sensed at once that by its means I would be delivered from my sorry state, and I smiled every time it was mentioned.

This first Christmas of mine was instructive in many ways. Besides teaching me to know the sufferings of illness, it taught me much else by keeping me in bed with nothing to do but look at what went on around me. I saw Mother clean our two rooms and wash the floors, beat the carpets, and shake the bedclothes. I was carried into the best room while my bed was aired and remade. Then as soon as the cleaning was finished, Mother set about the baking and cooking, but much more than usual. I don't remember just what food she did prepare, but during these days there was always the soft roar of a brisk fire burning in the range and on top of it two or three pots bubbled and steamed. From the oven wafted the smell of buns and rye bread, one batch after the other. Nor did Father have time to sit and rest in his rocking chair after he got home from work. First, he carried in pail after pail of water and filled the big wooden tub. Then he went down into the cellar beneath our floor and split large quantities of wood by candlelight. For a long, long time I could feel our floor shaking, and at last I saw Father carrying in armfuls and armfuls of firewood.

From the very start I had a feeling that the coming of Christmas was something remarkable; but while fighting against the exhaustion and soreness of my body I was not always up to watching what happened. Only later did the full meaning of what was going on become clear to me. Now and then I sank into a kind of torpid sleep, in which everything outside me vanished from sight and only my pain and tiredness were with me. Night and day lost their meaning, as my sleeping and waking did not follow them but went their own way. Mother, and Father too, had to get up many times in the night to stroke me and dry my hair and whisper soothing words.

The paths of sickness were confused and difficult, paths of punishment and darkness with only fitful gleams of light.

But suddenly I was free of my discomfort. I sank into a deep and dreamless sleep. I probably slept for a long time, but when I awoke I thought at first I had only closed my eyes for a moment. Looking round me, however, I saw that our two rooms had changed and were now fresh and festive. Both lamps were alight at the same time, and in addition our home was lighted by the candles burning on the branches of the decorated Christmas tree behind the door to the best room. The table was covered with a gleaming white cloth and was full of so many different kinds of savory food that it made my head swim just to look at it.

I was surrounded by a new light, the festive light of the dark time of year, the radiance of Christmas. I knew at once that it was protecting me with its gentle goodness and had already driven away the wickedness that had troubled me. I was still tired, but when my parents, sitting at the plentiful table, happened to glance at me, I smiled at them.

"Christmas is here now," I said quietly. "Just as you promised, Mother."

They jumped up from the table and rushed over to my bed.

"Are you better now?" Mother cried joyfully.

"He seems well enough," Father said, feeling my head. "And his hair is quite dry."

Mother brought something from the table, the sort of crisp, sweet thing I had always liked. But I didn't care for it now. I didn't want to eat, only to look.

"Just a little taste," Mother coaxed. "Just eat this little piece. I made it myself."

I merely smiled and shut my eyes again. I felt good and I knew that Christmas was all round me, though I did not look at it.

Mother and Father returned to the table and went on with their meal. I didn't understand half of what they said, but I somehow knew that they were talking cheerfully about me and believed I would soon be quite well. Only one thing did I take in clearly enough to be able to repeat it still. Mother said: "I have prayed the whole time for his life, and that is why God has been merciful to us. You should believe in Him too and pray that we never suffer another awful blow like when our first child died."

Only then did I hear that a girl had been born to our family before me, but that she had left this world before I arrived in it.

"Oh, I believe in God too," Father said, but his smile seemed rather vague. It was then the beginning of this century, when the old views of life still lived, but besieged by the new ones.

When I opened my eyes again some time later, they had finished their meal. Mother was clearing the table and getting ready to wash dishes. Father was standing in the middle of the floor, lighting an enormous cigar. That too was part of Christmas, as he didn't usually smoke such a thing, but satisfied his craving with a quid of tobacco. When he saw that I was awake again, he came up to me puffing at his cigar and said, "I wonder why Father Christmas is so long? Or hasn't Mother told you about him?"

I smiled and nodded. Yes, Mother had told me all kinds of things about him, though I still was not sure what sort of being he was. I had an idea, however, that in addition to being at least as good as Christmas he was also very jolly. Had I been stronger, I should certainly have been very curious about him, but I was too weak now to do anything but smile.

"I think I'll go out and see whether Father Christmas is already going the rounds of the house," Father said. "I'll try and get him to hurry up and come to us."

He gave me a slightly knowing look, his face flushed from eating and drinking, threw his best coat round his shoulders, and went out, hatless and puffing his cigar. Mother too seemed mysterious. She stood at the range washing up, saying something now and then and listening eagerly to what was going on outside. At last she went right over to the window and peered out into the dark yard.

"He's not at our steps yet."

I too tried to listen expectantly, but it taxed me too much. I lay there oblivious of whether time was passing or not. I made no effort to brighten up until I heard the thud of heavier steps than usual on the steps outside, like the sound of a giant's feet, and Mother exclaimed: "Now he's coming to us. What a pity Father isn't here to receive him!"

Mother took off her apron quickly and came and stood beside my bed. Our door was thrown open briskly, but no one entered. Perhaps Father Christmas thought that it wasn't worth showing himself to someone my size, and so remained standing in the dark hall. But he began tossing his presents towards my bed. Mother caught each package in the air, calling out eagerly who it was for. For you, my boy! And another, and a third. Ahaa, now I have a present, and another one! And here's a package for Father, though he isn't here to receive it. Now you again, my treasure—oh, what a big one! It must be a horse . . . Now for me . . . now for Father . . . and for you again. However many have you got?

That Christmas I certainly had more presents than ever before or since, though Father Christmas didn't show himself to me. Mother piled the parcels up on my quilt in a small mound. I watched the growing pile and the darkness behind the door out of which the presents came flying. The game seemed strange, even a little frightening, for I had not been able to make out from Father's and Mother's talk just what was happening.

But now I was so tired that not even fear bothered me very much. As the game went on, I closed my eyes again and my thoughts wandered off on their own. For a moment I forgot the extraordinary fact that it was now Christmas and that Father Christmas was throwing me his mysterious presents. All around me was summer, and now I dared to explore the meadow on the other side of the road. A lot of dandelions were growing there, and thick peat which had formed when the arm of the sea had dried up long, long ago and which squelched with every step I took. Warm summer water trickled sweetly between my toes. But I didn't get very far, as when the door suddenly banged shut I woke up again and opened my eyes with a start.

"Look what's here," Mother was saying. "A whistle shaped like a rooster, you blow it like this, see . . . And here are some brand-new winter boots for you. And here's a cap and here's a mouth organ . . ."

Suddenly Father appeared and began to examine the presents as eagerly as Mother. And I too tried to take another look at these things which had so suddenly materialized before me. I gazed at them in silence and touched some of them. Only when a large wooden horse stood before me and Father promised to let me get on its back when I was better, did I begin to grow excited. I seized it with both hands and snatched it into my arms. I had always loved horses, and now that I had one of my own, I forgot all my other presents.

I have no recollection of what kind of presents Father and Mother got that Christmas. The rest of my own presents were lost or broken in the days that followed, but this first horse of mine I have never forgotten. When I was well again and could get on the horse's back, I was very excited. I could ride on the kitchen floor wherever I liked and as far as my imagination could carry me. Under the horse's legs were rockers, and it was these that set me in motion and bore me from wall to wall.

But on this Christmas Eve I squeezed my horse's head under my arm with one hand and stroked its coarse mane with the other. Mother arranged it comfortably on my bed so that I didn't feel its weight. Having tired of their game, my parents sat down again at the table. Father picked up his thick bible, their wedding book, and began to read aloud in a monotonous voice. Mother sat opposite him, listening, her hands clasped.

When I shut my eyes again, I mounted my very own horse

and, to the accompaniment of Father's voice, galloped off across the summer meadow towards the mountain and the forests beyond.

III

When I could get up and Christmas was over, I became familiar with winter. For a long time I only looked at it. I would climb on a chair and gaze through the window at the strange, cold, white world outside. Sometimes Mother put a lot of clothes on me and let me out. But even then all I did was to stand in front of our steps, looking around me in astonishment. It was the snow that impressed me most; it had piled up even on the roofs, and our yard was now mysteriously transformed, with footpaths twisting between the drifts.

But I could only stand a little at a time looking and wondering at this strange winter. I soon began to feel cold. There was probably a very hard frost. In any case, I soon went back inside, took off all my extra clothes, and climbed on my horse's back. These rocking, clattering rides amused me more than anything else during these winter weeks. I started riding the minute I woke in the morning, I rode when Mother went off on her errands and I was left alone, I was still riding in the evening when Father came home from work, and I rode on until sleep overcame me.

Only later in the winter, as the air grew warmer with the approach of spring and the returning sun, and the paths grew wider and dirtier, did I begin to stay out longer and make my way to different parts of the yard. But I still didn't get very far, as the drifts made it impossible to move about except on the paths made through the snow. Anyone without skis could not get across it. So my memories of this time are few, and I can recall only one interesting event, which I witnessed at close quarters.

It was a lovely day, and I was standing on one of the highest points of our yard, when suddenly I saw two splendid horses turn off the street and dash into our yard with the snow whirling. They stopped right in front of my stout aunt's steps, and out of the wide, black, covered sleigh stepped a handsome woman dressed in furs. She looked at our house critically and as though wondering which steps she should mount. Nor did her fur-clad driver seem able to tell her where the people lived that she had come to see.

At the same moment the whole house began to seethe with excitement. Boys appeared from nowhere and surrounded the horses and the highbred strangers, almost dumb with admiration. Some of the women peeped through the curtains, but the more daring of them gathered in a group in the yard, some distance from the new arrival, and began to whisper together eagerly.

"It's the wife of the sawmill owner," someone said. "I'm sure it's his wife. I recognize her."

"What will Mrs. Lindström say now," whispered another.

"I knew all along something like this would happen," a third one croaked. "A working-class girl should know better than that."

Everyone seemed to guess why the grand lady had come to our house and everyone kept glancing at my Aunt Lindström's window as often as at her guest.

When she heard the jingle of the sleigh bells and the snorting of the horses, my aunt herself looked out of the window. Her face seemed to harden. But she did not come out, nor did she even stay at the window to gaze at the newcomer, but went on quietly with her work just as if nothing new and exciting were about to happen.

Having sized up the house and the people standing round her, the strange lady turned to the boy nearest her and asked where the Lindströms lived. The boy gave a start, straightened himself up, and then explained respectfully that the Lindströms' door and steps were just in front of her. The visitor turned to her coachman and ordered him to turn his horses towards the street.

"I shan't be long," she said, and began haughtily to mount the steps.

As I mentioned, I watched all that went on outside from the highest point of the yard, apart from the others. But when the lady began to go up the steps to my aunt's door, I move in my mind from the yard into my aunt's room. Perhaps I really did move inside just before the visitor, or else I'm imagining that I saw things which I only heard about later. Which is true? All I can say is that I have a clear picture of the stirring love drama that had taken place in my aunt's family.

Hearing the knock on the door, my aunt paused in her washing up and called out, a slight tremble in her voice:
"Come in!"

The door opened, and the haughty visitor appeared on the threshold. For a moment she seemed to wait for a respectful greeting, but when my aunt went on with her work without saying a word, the lady drew herself up and said:
"I am Mrs. Kristiansson."

"Oh, I know quite well who you are," my aunt replied, glancing at her. "Everybody knows you in this town. Please take a seat. I shall be finished in a moment."

The lady did not sit down but took a step nearer to my aunt.

"I suppose you can guess why I have come to see you?" she asked.

"Of course I can."

This is the conversation, or something like it, that comes into my mind from somewhere in the past. This fine lady and her husband did not live in the town, but their large sawmill was not far outside it. Their children went to school in the

46

town, and one of the sons was now seventeen. It was this lad who had fallen in love with the Lindströms' eldest daughter of sixteen, the one who worked in the fashionable milliner's. No doubt they had met in the main street, where the young people of the town, to the annoyance of the police, spent their evenings. Most of the marriages contracted at that time had their beginning on this street. No one thought any the worse of it, as the young people usually respected the class distinctions. But this was a rather shocking exception. The daughter of a common laborer and the son of a local dignitary had begun to keep company quite openly.

The reason why things had gone as far as this was that on weekday evenings there was only a maidservant to keep an eye on the lad, and he took no notice of what she said. The matter was the talk of the town before it reached the ears of the boy's parents, and in their view this only made it worse. The boy was fetched home in midweek and severely questioned, with the result that he was not sent back to school. But this did not put an end to the young people's love. Every day a strange and proud-looking letter arrived at the girl's home, in which the youth assured her of his continued devotion in spite of his parents' wishes. The girl now spent every evening reading them over and over again, weeping with sorrow and joy. That is why the lad's wealthy mama had deigned to call in person at this humble home.

So now she was standing in the Lindströms' kitchen, while her spirited horses pawed the snowy ground in our yard. No wonder all our neighbors were waiting with bated breath to see what would happen. Because the affair was common knowledge, I too can tell of it as if I had taken part in it all.

I have already said that the visitor was a handsome, haughty woman. But at this moment my aunt, for all her bulk, held herself proudly too. I seem to think that the following conversation took place.

"You ought to realize that my boy's future is very dear to me. He's still a schoolboy, a mere child. I think it most improper that he should go about with a girl at that age."

"So do I. A man should have some kind of profession before he goes putting ideas into a girl's head."

"You should have forbidden your daughter to see my son. Don't you realize that she is running a big risk."

"If you can separate them, I'd be very grateful to you. I can't."

"Oh, can't you!"

"I can't chain my daughter up!"

My aunt finished washing the dishes and began to dry her hands. Having glanced at herself instinctively, she noticed that her apron was dirty. She took it off quickly and threw it behind the woodbox as though to hide it.

"We could of course transfer Arthur to a school in another town," the visitor said after a moment, "but in the middle of term like this it would be bad for his studies. As it is, his teachers say that he has not been doing at all well lately."

"Naturally not, when he runs after the girl every evening and part of the night as well," my aunt retorted.

The visitor tapped her small foot impatiently. Didn't the woman realize whom she was speaking to?

"Where is your daughter?" she exclaimed. "I want a word with her."

"At work, of course. The poor girl has her set hours."

Mrs. Kristiansson swung round so quickly that the ends of her wide furs flapped. An almost stifling cloud of sweet scent was wafted even into my nostrils. She adjusted the silk bands of her muff. She knew of better measures to take for her boy's good than to waste time in this working-class home. Strong measures.

She raised her head loftily and left the room. I rushed to the window. The coachman was standing ready beside the

48

sleigh, holding up the edge of the rug, as she came down the steps, and he helped her in. Then he climbed onto his box as nimbly as his large fur coat allowed. The horses snorted, the bells jingled, and the sleigh dashed out of the yard into the street in a flurry of snow, as the neighbors' children flung themselves out of the way into the drifts.

As I craned my neck after the sleigh, I saw that the sky was a dismal gray, and I heard my aunt sobbing quietly in the room behind me.

The flock of women in the yard grew larger. They were chattering excitedly and nodding their heads, now at our windows and now towards the town, while the boys and girls played at being horses and showed how splendidly they had galloped off.

I don't know how long my aunt wept, nor have I any idea what happened that day in the fashionable milliner's. But a clear picture of my aunt's eldest daughter forms in my mind. As time went on, she grew pale and thin, becoming more beautiful day by day. She no longer talked to anybody, and at the dinner table did not even answer her father's eager questions. Up to now these meal-time conversations had been one of the highlights of the family's daily life, and now they too faded. For many weeks the girl's misery spread around her like a dark cloud, and for this reason I could not go and see them for a long time.

Later, however, the two young people were married. Some years afterwards I met them in another house and for a little while this same young man became my friend.

IV

At this time I felt closer to Mother than to Father. Sometimes in the evenings, when Father came home from work, I would still long for the vanished world and climb up into his arms in the rocking chair. But the old familiar father no longer existed; he had swum away from me, far out to sea. I enjoyed rocking in this present father's arms; but as he never told me anything about invisible lands far away, I soon got tired of him. I would jump down on to the floor again, climb on to my horse's back, and ride away at full speed wherever my imagination took me.

On Sunday mornings I always found this present father in bed; he stayed there long after Mother had set about her chores and I had gone out. Not until lunch was ready did he too get up and put on his Sunday best, and after the meal he usually went off somewhere for most of the afternoon.

But when the spring came and the sun warmed the world around us, he asked me to go with him on one of these after-lunch excursions. I was very excited. I had a feeling that today I would experience something new and thrilling.

We set off, and walked past a lot of houses and near the church, but not on the same side as when I passed it for the first time in my very early youth. Beyond the church, however, we came on to the road I knew and when we got to the bottom of the hill I saw the harbor again and heard the deep whistles of the steamers. We did not stop where my first outing had ended, but went round to the other side of the steep rock, where all at once I saw a lot of houses I didn't know, ornamented houses that seemed to me very big, and last of all a gay-looking kiosk. And there we met a stranger, a very nice, laughing young man. Who was he, I wonder? My memory tells me nothing about him except his laugh, his youth, and the fact that it was he who sat me down at the kiosk's only table and put lemonade and cakes in front of me.

"You stay here by yourself for a little while," Father said. "We'll be back soon."

"You can watch the harbor, the ships and the sea," the stranger said, "and eat and drink all you want."

50

They whispered to the kiosk woman to keep an eye on me while they went to the hotel for a drink of their own.

I heard them say all this, but it didn't worry me. The lemonade and cakes, and above all the splendid sights, quite made up to me for being alone. I soon forgot where I was and who had brought me here. I looked about me and I listened to all the sounds of land, sea, and sky. When the woman tried to talk to me, since there were not many customers down by the harbor on a Sunday, I listened with only half an ear. I was always a silent child, and at the moment all I wanted to do was to concentrate on looking at and listening to the world around me and to absorb all these new impressions. So I forced the woman to be still. I must become familiar with all the new, hitherto unknown things from farther away. New secrets were hidden in the midst of the harbor, the bay, the forest glimpsed beyond the sea in the distance, the clouds, and sun and the sky. It was the quiet, Sunday traffic in the harbor and on the water that made me sense that something lay concealed behind the visible shapes and signs, and it was these vital, fascinating secrets that I tried to unravel.

I did not know then, and cannot explain now, just what I felt. From the outset my mind, my whole mental being, was raised to a glorious, dizzy state of happiness. I was oblivious of the passing of time and don't remember how long I sat there, though the lemonade and cakes were soon all gone. I didn't really get any nearer to the secrets until I stopped eating and the woman stopped talking. Sitting there, quiet and still, I was aware of something rich and exalted pouring into me.

When Father and the stranger at last came back to me from the hotel on the other side of the road, I almost shrank from them at first. They were in very good spirits, talking and joking together, their eyes sparkling, their cheeks flushed. Even my father, my quiet father, was behaving in this extraordinary way. It didn't worry or annoy me, however; it was simply that, now that they had come back, I had to leave my secret journeys and all the new sights and sounds. I had to answer their questions: Yes, I've been all right, I've had a nice time, I enjoyed the lemonade and cakes. I had to listen to all that they had been doing, but I couldn't make it out at all, any more than I could understand why the kiosk woman was laughing at them in that funny way.

But after the stranger had left us and Father and I were on our way home, I still tried to hold on moment by moment to the fading memory of my secret experiences. Now that there were only the two of us, Father made no attempt to talk to me, nor did he disturb me in any other way, so I might have had a chance to recapture them. But I didn't succeed very well. The nearer we came to home, the more they faded away. I was so unhappy about this that Father, walking along lost in thought, at last noticed I was looking miserable. He eyed me for a moment, then took my hand.

"Come on, cheer up," he said. "Let's not go home yet. We'll go over there to the edge of the woods and make whistles and blow them."

Perhaps he thought I was sad because he had left me alone for so long and now wanted to cheer me up before taking me back to Mother. I looked at him doubtfully. I didn't yet know about willow whistles. But when I saw him smiling, I brightened.

"Yes, let's."

We went a little way past our house. On the right was a small house much older than ours, and on the left the meadow ended in a dense clump of alders. We pushed our way into it. The ground was damp, and water oozed from under our shoes as we went farther into the grove. When it thinned out and the ground became drier and covered with mossy stones, Father stopped. We seemed to be hidden away in a very quiet, warm spot. My recent sadness was forgotten

52

and I suddenly felt all right again. The voices of people in the street did not reach as far as this. There was nothing to be seen but the sky, and the sun shining down seemed very near.

"Sit here," Father said, "while I go and look for some willows."

He pushed about this way and that for some time in the thicket, looking for thin willows among the alders. When he came back to me, he had a large bunch of them in his hand. He sat down beside me, took the sheath knife from his belt, and set to work. I watched attentively, curious to see what would come from his hands. First, the willow switch was sliced off obliquely where it was flat and smooth, then a thin ring of bark was removed, and into the space left above it an airhole was cut. This piece of bark was slowly and carefully loosened by tapping it evenly with the handle of the knife and by holding it several times in the mouth. When this bark came away, a deep, wide groove was cut into the wood underneath it—straight on the "mouth" side and semicircular on the other side. From the sharp, straight edge a thin, even cut was made as far as the outer edge. It was along this that the air was blown so that it reached the inside. The unbroken bark was replaced and the whistle raised to the lips. A sweetly piercing sound rose suddenly into the air, a sound that was a little shrill but somehow gay and mischievous.

It startled me, and I listened tensely to this strange music. Where did it come from? Just what was it telling me? I sensed at once that I had been drawn by chance to the edge of a circle into which I would never be admitted, but despite this I wanted to listen to the strange sounds to learn something of what was within it. Although Father smiled as he looked at me, and at last burst out laughing, I remained serious. When the music stopped with his laughter, I called out excitedly: "Don't stop! Go on blowing! Blow, blow, please!"

I shouted this many, many times. Whenever he tried to

stop, I begged him to go on, until he too grew serious and stopped playing.

"I don't know how to play," he said. "You have a try."

The whistle was pressed to my lips and Father told me how to press my lips round the whistle and blow into the hole. After a little while I could really do it, and into the air rose music that came from my mouth. Although it was softer, simpler, and less colorful than the sounds Father had made, it too delighted me. Time and again I played in order to hear what kind of unfamiliar sounds would well up from inside me.

In the meantime Father was making new whistles from the willows he had brought, big ones and small, and he kept handing them to me.

"Try this one! Try this!"

I tried, and was startled again and again, because from each whistle came a different sound. What did it mean? That the sound did not come from me at all, but from somewhere else, perhaps far away? I was only the medium through which the unknown power passed as it became audible to humans. And every time I took a new whistle, I became the instrument of an entirely new kind of being. It was very disturbing.

Father looked at me curiously and began to laugh more than ever. "Don't be frightened," he said. "They're merry, good folk who are coming to us now."

We spent a long time there in our quiet, warm hiding place. We blew our whistles the whole time, Father and I by turns. Gradually I began to notice the signs of spring around me. I saw that the alders and willows had tiny, beautifully bright leaves, that the moss crept over the rocks dressed in its dark but gay colors, and that here and there between the rocks grew fresh blades of grass and small white and blue flowers, the spring anemones. Perhaps it was the music flowing through us which taught me these things. At all events I

54

began to fear it less and love it more as time went on. Though I came no nearer to the secrets of the music, I began to think that it represented merry, good folk, just as Father had said.

This day indeed turned out to be one of the loveliest days of my young life. After a long time I had seen the harbor again, I listened to the voices of the whistles, I learned to know the lushness and beauty of the earth's plants, the blue of the sky, and the swiftness of the thin clouds. I began to sense that they belonged together and that, in fact, I too was part of them. For a moment I came close to Father again, just as I had done before when I was quite tiny, and it was he who led me to these things. I have forgotten all the words, but I can still recall the mood whenever I think of it.

When at last we rose from our warm hiding place and went home, Mother was standing anxiously in the street near the house.

"Where have you been all day?" she exclaimed. "I thought you had both been drowned in the harbor."

Father grasped her arm and laughed. "We've been blowing whistles," he said. "And the lad will play for you at home. He has an armful of them."

That day I could do nothing but blow my whistles, even inside. I sat down in the corner beside my horse and raised one whistle after the other to my lips to hear their joyful sounds. I was so taken up with them that I had no mind even to eat. I just went on playing until day changed to evening and I grew tired. Then Mother undressed me and put me to bed, but I took my whistles with me as I went off to the land of sleep.

v

When I woke up in the morning Father had already gone to work as usual and my whistles had withered and were almost silent. So I too had to begin my ordinary weekdays. At first, however, I didn't really believe it; I tried to cling to Sunday for all I was worth. I pestered Mother for a clasp knife and rushed to the clump of alders, to the same spot where Father and I had sat. But by the time I had whittled several willow switches and spoiled them, I began to understand that yesterday was gone forever.

Instead, I made friends with someone who was to be my playmate for many weeks.

On my way back from the alders to the street I met a sturdy boy of my own size who lived in a small, old house. He began by throwing stones at me, but when he saw that I was timid he soon made friends. Our stone fight changed into throwing stones into the meadow, and as I did quite well at this it became a kind of competition. We spent many hours in the street looking for the right size stones in the sandy surface and flinging them first in one direction, then in another. When we got tired we sat down in the gutter to brag, then started throwing again. Only once or twice did someone drive past in a cart; and as there were very few people walking about, it was a good place to be.

So our first day of friendship passed. Next day, and on many, many other days, we met in the street. As soon as I came out in the morning I would rush to his house to meet him. We didn't bother about throwing stones after the first day, but started exploring instead. My playmate was already far more familiar with the world than I was and he knew his way around.

It was thanks to him that I came to know the old village on the far side of the meadow. In those days it had a bad name, and Mother had often warned me against going there. I did, nevertheless, whenever my pal went, and I found out how the nettles stung my legs and arms, how almost every cottage had a potato patch, and how drunk the men used to get on beer.

56

There were also young boys and girls who yelled and fought, cats and dogs that had fish and bones thrown to them, and old women with big swollen bellies. In other words, the old village was an exciting place which I explored eagerly.

We did not make friends with the village boys or with anyone else. We just ran about from cottage to cottage and from one yard to the next, looking at everything and everybody like strangers, and always making off the minute danger threatened. There was only one old woman we bothered to speak to sometimes. I heard that she was my pal's aunt, a hard, stern woman. Nearly every time we stopped at her cottage we saw her set her grandson, a boy of about our age, to clean fish. The rest of her family were all dead, and as they were the only two left they had to live on whatever fish they could catch.

I did not yet understand poverty and real sorrow, although it was only a few years before they were to afflict me too. I just felt rather sorry for this boy, who could not be free like us. Nor did I understand that this dangerous village was a dying part of the town, with nineteenth-century habits and customs that were doomed to vanish.

Once we went farther afield. Somewhere behind the village we came upon a road and some woods that looked quite strange to me, surrounded by a tumbledown fence. The trees all had lush green foliage—it was early summer—and had a cared-for look compared with the rest of the forest. Some of them were old and gnarled, others mere saplings, with a few flowering shrubs here and there. Between the trees a sandy road, now overgrown with grass, had been made, leading to a rather grand house that could be glimpsed through the trees. The first time we went there my playmate told me to run past the house as fast as I could, explaining afterwards, out of breath and whispering, that the place belonged to an old and frightening baroness. She was frightening because in that very house the Freemasons used to meet by candlelight with daggers in their hands. The baroness' maid had seen all this through a half-open door and had told her friends about it in a scared whisper.

I didn't quite understand what was meant by all this, but for that very reason it made the place exciting and frightening indeed. Ordinary people didn't use candles for light, but oil lamps; nor did they wear daggers at their belts, but ordinary, practical sheath knives. And although there was not a soul to be seen in the house or the overgrown garden, not even the servant or her footprints, my whole body began to shake.

It was by far the most interesting place I found that summer, but even later I did not dare to explore it more closely, and the vague and mysterious impression I had of it remained far off, inexplicable, and on the other side of a dividing boundary.

Another day we went in the opposite direction, towards the center of the town, and found a deep, wide ditch, part of an old canal that had been filled in here and there. At the bottom of it was some green, evil-smelling water, and its sides were covered with thick weeds and shrubbery. It was on the edge of this ditch that we once came upon a group of boys, fifteen or sixteen years old, who had cigarettes in their mouths and knives at their belts and who were playing cards. I found out that one of them was my playmate's eldest brother. Here I learned a lot of new words which I had never heard at home. I thought these new words, and also the way these youths behaved, were very exciting and interesting.

On another of our excursions we did not go to the village at all, but to the same clump of alders where I had learned to blow whistles. We pushed right through the alders and came to the forest proper and the steep slope of the rocks. When we climbed up between the moss-covered boulders, our range of vision suddenly widened out. Down below us lay meadow and street, village and woods, the houses where we lived and lots of other houses and streets, and the church in all its splendor on its own hill. The view was so vast that I was speechless and dizzy. For a long time I was unable to say anything, only gaze.

Had we gone any farther, we should have come to still bigger pine trees and still higher rocks and boulders which we could just see in the distance. We had to climb down the same way we had got up, as the other side of the rock was so steep that not even moss could grow there. So all we did on this outing was to climb up, gaze rapt and silent at the view, and go back to the alders and from there to the street.

In this way time passed, spring changed to summer. My playmate had already seen all the places that he now showed to me and could explain the meaning of my new discoveries and all their secrets. The leaves of the trees became broader and denser and gradually lost their scent. The first spring flowers vanished and in their place other flowers appeared in the meadow, in the yards of the houses, and in the woods. The mass of stalks and leaves in all the potato patches shot up higher and higher, and the uncut hay began to wither. Only then did Mother notice a change in my speech; she kept asking me where I spent my time and put a sudden stop to my excursions. At first she sharply forbade me to see any more of my playmate, as he too was one of the village children though he lived near us. In spite of this, however, I ran off to meet him as soon as I was let out. Mother ran after me, hurried me home, and for the first time gave me a whipping. That was the end of our friendship. Sometimes, months later, when Mother no longer watched me, I would go along the street to wait for him outside his house, but he was not to be seen.

59

It was years before I met him again. One winter we were in the same class at school, and later we used to nod to each other in the street, but our friendship was never renewed.

VI

When the summer was well advanced, Mother took me with her one day on an outing of her own. She borrowed a handcart from somewhere, loaded it up with dirty clothes, firewood, food, and a large copper cauldron, and off we went to the same seashore where I once swam with Father, though not quite to the same spot.

The shore we came to was on a small inlet and from there the sea looked like a lake. Here too there were boulders, but they were not very big, and in between them were smooth patches of grass; fine stretches of sand continued out under the water until they were lost to sight. I was fascinated by everything I found, perhaps most of all by the fact that three other women had already arrived to do their washing and had lighted fires under their tubs. It was a hot day and the sea lay motionless. Not a breath of wind stirred the leaves of the bushes or rippled the surface of the water. The smoke from the fires burning under the clothes boilers rose straight up towards the sky like stiff, heavy pillars. It was high, high up before it dispersed and vanished into the air.

There were a lot of children here too. While Mother was unloading, making a suitable fireplace out of stones, carrying water from the sea, and lighting her own fire, I ran about with the other children. When they undressed and went for a swim, I went with them. Some of them waded out where it was deep and began to dog-paddle. That was the only way to swim known here in those days. We smaller ones stayed near the shore, where the sand was soft and warm and the water reached only to our knees.

So the day began, and it went on like this almost until evening. When we had swum and splashed about to our hearts' content, we ran and threw ourselves down full length in the sand. I have no recollection whatever of who the other children were or what they were like, but I can see myself lying in the midst of a large group, now watching their antics, now gazing up at the sky or away over the water, now listening to the gay chatter of the washerwomen and the slap of the clothes. Then, when the others tired of the land and rushed back into the water, I rushed with them. We all had a special feeling of well-being, far above the way we felt on ordinary days.

At one stage of her work Mother put a small coffeepot to boil beside the washtub and after a while she called to me to come and eat. She gave me a large cup of hot coffee and several big sandwiches, which tasted better than ever before. I ate one after the other, far more than on most days. The other mothers and their children all did the same, but at different times, according to how their work was getting on.

It was late in the afternoon when I got a sudden warning that life is not all roses. At first I went swimming just as before, but when I saw the bigger boys and girls wading far out and some of them swimming still farther, I too was overcome by the urge to go on and on. Leaving those of my age with their own group, I set off after the others. Step by step I waded forward, feeling the water at the bottom get colder and the surface creep up my body, first to my thighs, then to my stomach, and right up to my chest and armpits. Then I stopped and let out a wild shout of joy and victory, splashing the water all round me as hard as I could. All the children noticed me and those of my age at any rate stopped to watch in both envy and admiration. Unfortunately the women were so busy at their hard work that they didn't happen to look our way just then.

When I had rejoiced for a while over my accomplishment and success, I felt I had to achieve a still greater victory. I waded forward a few steps more and suddenly the ground vanished from under my feet. With a rush the water came right to the tip of my uptilted chin, the tips of my toes touched the loose sandy bottom for a second and then not even that. I heard my companions give a frightened yell and in some way I was aware that the women screamed too and that Mother dashed to the water's edge towards me. Water poured into my mouth and nostrils and for a moment I thought I was drowning. I now knew the meaning of that word. But a second later I was filled with new strength. I started kicking and thrashing about as I had seen swimmers do, but in a frenzied way, as though I had been storing up secret life forces which had to find an outlet. And before long, just as I felt utterly exhausted, I felt my feet touch bottom. I could do nothing else but stand where I was, breathing heavily and sputtering water.

No one could do anything to help me, but Mother waded out with all her clothes on. When she reached me she snatched me into her arms and carried me to the shore, across the beach to the grassy patch behind the boulders. There she lay me down on the ground and cried out:

"Are you all right? There's nothing wrong with you?"

"Yes, I'm all right," I answered, closing my eyes.

After about ten minutes I sat up, then scrambled to my feet feeling quite myself again. All the washerwomen and all the children were standing round me, talking excitedly. When they saw there was no cause for alarm, they began to move away. Mother went on looking at me anxiously for some time, but having come to the same conclusion she too went back to her work, saying sternly:

"You're not to go into the water any more, do you hear. If you do, I'll spank you."

Mother no doubt thought that since I myself had invited danger, she must now be cross with me.

Still naked, I went to lie down in the sand with the others and listen to their talk. I imagined that all was well and that life was wonderful. But gradually I began to feel that something was wrong. I tried to think it was because I couldn't go swimming any more with the others, and a little later because the fires started to go out and our group dwindled. One of the washerwomen packed up her things on her handcart, called to her children, and set off for home. Before long another did the same. I also noticed that the sun was beginning to make long shadows beside the bushes and boulders, as it sank lower and lower towards the skyline behind which it usually disappeared for the night. Things like this indeed gave cause for sorrow.

But however stubbornly I tried to fix my attention outside myself, I was still aware of the tiredness and aching in my body, which was getting worse every moment. As the minutes went by, I was less and less able to look at things going on outside me. They seemed to be moving farther and farther away, growing dim, and at last vanishing somewhere into the dark.

One of the other women, on her way past us to get water, suddenly stopped to look at me, then exclaimed to Mother, "That boy of yours looks quite ill. He has a temperature, I'm sure."

Mother left off her work and rushed up to me again. "What's wrong with the poor boy now?"

"He's had too much sun," the woman said. "Our children have been running about naked and swimming ever since the spring, so the sun does them good. But your little lad was quite white when you undressed him. Now all the skin will peel off his back at least. You should've been more careful."

"Heavens above!" Mother cried. "He's all hot!"

63

"Put his clothes on and take him into the shade. He'll be all right there until you've finished your washing."

Mother dressed me quickly and carried me into the shade of some young alders. I tried to resist and pretend that this was even more unfair than forbidding me to swim, but actually I was quite content with my new spot. It was much nicer here than on the sandy beach. The silence did me good. I closed my eyes and all I could hear were the uneasy throbbing sounds of my body.

When Mother came back to me some time later, I was dimly aware that the shadows had lengthened and the sun had sunk still nearer the horizon. Mother lifted me up and said encouragingly, "Come along, dear, try now to walk home, and I'll give you something nice that will soon make you well."

Gripping the handcart, I tottered home. Mother undressed me quickly, gave me something hot to drink, and put me to bed, to wander about all night along those same strange paths that I had traveled when Christmas came.

VII

When this eventful summer came to an end, I learned about autumn too, but not where I usually lived. Mother took me with her on a journey.

Mother was rather sad all day before we left. She still smiled and laughed, but it was different from before. At the time I didn't realize that she was recalling her childhood and the home of her youth. In the evening Father came to the station to see us off, and I saw a train for the first time. He lifted our luggage into the carriage, but when the train started he waved to us from the platform and was soon lost to sight. We sat there listening to the buzz of strangers' conversation and the clatter and roar of the train. When it was so late that at home I would have been asleep long ago, I fell asleep even here, too tired to take in any more of the strange things I was seeing. When Mother shook me awake in the morning, we were at our destination.

We were met by a laughing young man whom I had to call Uncle; he had with him a brown, yellow-maned horse which snorted and whinnied and pawed the ground in front of the light, yellow gig. Uncle helped us up onto the front seat with our luggage, and he sat behind us. Then he picked up the reins, the horse's mane and tail fluttered, and away we went at a spanking pace. In my fright I gripped the edge of the gig with both hands, though Mother was squeezing me against her and exclaiming half in alarm, half in delight, "Don't drive so fast, you madcap. You'll be the death of us."

But Uncle merely laughed in our ears, "Our girls have never been afraid of a drive. Or have you become so soft there in town that you can't keep your seat? But whoever comes for a drive with the Pietola stallion must make the best of it."

And the stallion flew on, its mane and tail streaming, its hooves striking sparks from the stones. The road, with already a touch of autumn about it, was hard and damp. Chill, dark-gray clouds sailed in the low-hanging, pale blue sky. The crows flew cawing across the wet fields. People with large baskets and dressed in their oldest clothes were bent double, digging potatoes. A plowman was plodding along behind his horse and plow. The rowan, maple, and birch trees growing round the houses and in the hollows flamed in all their autumn coloring. Drops of water fell from the ends of the dark-green branches of the firs. Now and then the sun slipped out between the breaks in the clouds and shed a wan light over the landscape. Here for the first time I was aware that autumn had come to the world; in any case, I felt I had arrived in a region that was strange to me.

As we drove over a small bridge, under which the water

rippled in black eddies, Mother wanted to stop for a moment. We got down from the gig, and Uncle tied the horse to the rail. Mother began to walk up and down, furtively brushing tears from the corners of her eyes and at the same time taking a few dance steps. At last she stopped by the rail and gazed down at the black water.

"Do you still dance here on the bridge?" she asked.

"Do you imagine gaiety deserted our village just because you ran off to town and got married?" Uncle said.

Mother stared down at the water for a long time, wiping away many tears. I looked away, so that she would not feel ashamed because of me. Not far away I saw a lake; the surface gleamed the color of clay and the reeds by the shore glowed like ripe cornfields. A large flock of birds flew across the sky.

"They're off to the south, to the warm lands," Uncle said when he noticed me watching them.

At last Mother got back into the gig. The man lifted me up beside her and climbed up behind us. Our spirited young horse set off again. But for a long time Mother did not say anything; her eyes were fixed ahead dreamily, far, far into the distance where I could not follow.

Before long the horse turned off the road into a lane leading to a small, modern farm. This was where Uncle lived. A young woman and two girls of my age appeared on the steps of the house to receive us. Mother jumped down and rushed towards the woman with open arms. They gazed into each other's eyes, laughing with joy and weeping at the same time.

"So I'm able to see you again at last, the best friend of my childhood," the strange woman exclaimed.

"And I you," Mother sobbed.

"You're not a day older. The years have merely made you more beautiful than ever."

66

"What about you? The prettiest farmer's wife in the district since you married the heir to Pietola."

Actually, Mother and her friend expressed their feelings in different words, in a more old-fashioned, country dialect than I now use. But I can only describe their conversation in my own words and hope you will forgive me.

When I was lifted down from the gig, I watched the little girls with great interest, and they paid far more attention to me than to my mother. We were too shy, however, to make friends immediately.

We spent the whole day there. We had dinner at a huge, splendid table. We went to see the animals—a large angry sow which had seven piglets, pretty, bleating lambs, three cows which sighed softly and heavily as they went on munching hay and gazing at us with wondering, gentle eyes. We even saw the horse in its stable, but only from a distance. We were told it was wild and did not like strangers.

"It takes a man to manage Pietola's horses and daughters," Uncle said with a laugh.

But Mother replied gravely, "I've never been one of Pietola's daughters. I was only a servant."

He glanced at her and grew serious, but said nothing. He was one of the rightful heirs of the farm to which we were going.

Next morning the horse with the cream-colored mane was harnessed again to the gig. Mother and I got up into the front seat with our luggage and Uncle behind us. The horse tossed its mane, snorted, and broke into a trot. The road continued level and dry for a long time across a heath with tall, straight pines and gleaming red cranberries. The sky was even more gloomy and low-hanging than the day before, and now and then it flung short, cold rainshowers at us. The high tops of the pines swayed and moaned in the wind; it sounded as though the whole of space were playing on a mighty organ. One flock of birds after the other flew past, to the south, to the warm lands. Mother was silent and thoughtful. Uncle did not speak either. I realized more clearly than yesterday what autumn meant.

After a long time we came again to tilled fields, through which flowed a narrow, clayey river. Beyond the river the ground rose to a kind of ridge. At the top was a house. I guessed at once that it was Pietola, the house where Uncle had grown up and where Mother too had spent several years of her life. It was large and gray and had a lot of small windows. Growing in front of it were two enormous birches, whose sparse foliage seemed to darken the whole sky and whose bark was full of deep grooves in which moss was growing. The house appeared to look down proudly, almost contemptuously, on the world from its high position. One could see at once that it was used to being above others, above the humans who even now were hard at work in the muddy fields. The people stooping in the potato fields were like black insects, and the men plowing the stubble did not look much better. And we who were approaching the house had to drive for a long time uphill; sturdy, spirited horse though it was, it had little desire to snort after the steep pull.

On the wide gray porch there was only one person, an old woman, gray and small like a mouse. As the horse stopped in front of the steps she got to her feet with the aid of her stick and gazed at us in silence, her chin trembling slightly. Mother rushed up to her and hugged her.

"Mother, mother!" she cried, her eyes full of tears.

Then she took my arm and drew me solemnly in front of the old woman.

"This is my son."

The old lady's crooked hand brushed my head and her chin began to tremble more than ever.

68

"He's a sturdy lad," she said. "He looks like one of us, even if he has strange blood in him."

Mother was the second youngest of a large family, so by this time Grandmother was very old and ailing.

We went inside, into large, silent rooms smelling of smoke and old, worm-eaten wood. The living room–kitchen was so huge that I could hardly make out the far wall. The stove was black and looked as big as a mountain. Beside it stood a buxom woman stirring a large pot. In the other rooms were massive beds, large cupboards and chests, tables, benches, and in one room a leather-bound book, an alarmingly large, heavy book. I hardly dared to walk through these rooms except on tiptoe.

Just what was this house, I wonder? Grandmother was taken from there to her grave, and Mother had been a dairy-maid and servant there at one time. Perhaps in reality it was not at all how I remember it. At any rate it was said to have been quite a prosperous farm.

When Uncle left us, Mother and I were alone. Grandmother had stayed in the big kitchen.

Mother sat down on the wide, thick wooden bed and looked at me smilingly, at the same time trying to keep back her tears, as she had done the day before on the bridge where there had been dancing.

"I slept in this room for many years," she said. "I was a dairymaid and servant girl then. It was from this room that I set off for the town where we now live."

We sat in this room for a long time without saying anything in particular. Once Mother got up and looked out of the window at the fields, above which the crows flapped, cawing in the wind. Then she sat down again on the bed and remained lost in thought until we were called to dinner.

We stayed in this house for many days and many nights. Years later I heard that we went off once or twice to see

Mother's brothers and sisters, but I remember nothing about them. I have not even the vaguest recollection of what they looked like. They have meant nothing to me. But there are a lot of things I can tell about this house.

Here I met, apart from my grandmother, an elderly man whom I was told to call Uncle. He was the master of this big old house. There were several women here too, some elderly and some very young, and two boys only a little older than myself. I also met another old man who was constantly chewing tobacco; his trousers hung down so low that at first I was always expecting them to fall to the floor. There were more of the yellow-maned horses in the stable, a large number of cows in the barn, and pigs in the pigsty. In fact there were all kinds of interesting things here, but the whole time I was fascinated most of all by my old grandmother, though for days on end she usually did nothing but sit by the window, gazing out. If I went right up to her, she would often put her hand on my head and say those same mysterious words:

"Yes, you're one of us all right. Even if you do have strange blood."

These words sounded solemn and frightening, they stirred the very depths of my being and made me feel I was an extraordinary creature.

During these days Mother seemed to forget entirely that she was a married woman from the town. She took off all her town clothes, put on high boots and an old skirt and blouse she had found in the servants' quarters above the hayloft, and went off with the others to dig potatoes. She seemed quite wild. Shrieking with laughter, she leaped over fences and ditches, climbed on to a yellow-maned horse's back and galloped along the road so fast that the horse's hooves struck sparks from the stones. In the evenings, other young women and girls gathered round her, even from the neighboring farms, and they laughed and giggled until late into the night.

70

And on Saturday night, the first Saturday night of my life, the local fiddler came to the house, a man with only one eye, and in addition to the girls there were a lot of strange young men. Mother danced with them, one after the other, and almost forgot me for the entire evening.

Outside it was autumn, autumn. The wind howled and moaned round the house on the hill day and night. The yellow leaves went with it, far away to the wet fields where the crows were cawing. In the gray sky flock after flock of birds flew to the south, to the warm lands.

And all the time the little gray grandmother sat in her solid chair by the window, staring out. I was sure she sat there all night too, because she was still there when I went to bed and already in her chair in the morning when I woke up. She was as quiet and gray as a mouse, but I sensed that it was she who was the most important part of my origin. Perhaps, as I gazed at her, I began to think of bigger things, even to wonder whether man's beginning and end were more than what we merely see with our eyes. Every day Grandmother repeated the mysterious, frightening, and impressive words: "You're one of us, but you have strange blood in you."

But on the morning of our departure Grandmother got up from her chair and came to the porch, where she had been standing when we arrived. She stood leaning on her stick, her chin trembling slightly. Mother embraced her with tears in her eyes. "Mother, Mother, I wonder if I'll ever see you again!" she exclaimed.

I still have a clear picture of Grandmother's wrinkled face and bent shoulders. Once more she put her hand on my head and repeated the same words: "You're one of us. But you have strange blood in you."

This time it was the elderly master of the house who drove us in the gig. The yellow-maned horse's mane and tail streamed in the wind and its hooves began to strike sparks from the stones in the road. Once the wind rushing towards us snatched the cap from my head and the horse had to stop for a moment. The cap was lying among the heather and the cranberries, and as soon as it was found the horse broke into a canter again. This time we went straight to the station.

For a long time Mother was very quiet and serious. Perhaps she was thinking of her own mother, my grandmother. But after we got on the train she began to laugh and smile again. That is all I remember of our journey home, for I must have fallen asleep as quickly as I did when we first set out.

VIII

The autumn was already far advanced. The rain pelted down from the gray clouds hanging over the town, the plants vanished entirely, the days grew shorter and shorter and the nights longer and longer. But the most important thing this autumn was not what I noticed of the world about me, but what happened to Mother.

One morning when I woke up, Mother was not at home; beside the bed stood my pockmarked aunt. She smiled at me and said, "Up you get, young man. I'll dress you and take you over to us for breakfast."

I started up in bed, looked about me, even glanced into the other room, but Mother was nowhere to be seen. My aunt laughed so that her fat belly wobbled. "Mother went to get you a baby brother or sister," she said at last. "You're going to spend the next few days with us. Your father will come and bring you home in the evenings."

I was very restless in the days that followed. Auntie fed me well, giving me as much as I could possibly eat, but otherwise she had no time to keep me company. I wandered about the yard and the house as though in search of something. With Mother away, life seemed insecure. I was bored and miserable and didn't even want to be with people. I mooned about from one place to the next, every now and then running inside to my aunt to ask the time and if Father would soon be home. I had never noticed before that time could pass so slowly that it seemed as if day and night had stopped dead in their tracks.

Father always came home so late that the world outside had been dark for a long time. When he finished work he went to see Mother every day before coming to fetch me from my aunt's. Then he led me home across the dark yard, undressed me, and put me straight to bed. For the first few days he looked so sad that I didn't dare to ask him anything about Mother, but shut my eyes at once so as to get into the lovely safe world of dreams as fast as possible.

But one evening Father was all smiles and came in carrying cakes and sweets. He was talkative and gay and kept telling my aunt, her husband and children, "I've another son now. A fine strong lad, much stronger than this first one."

When asked how Mother was, he looked serious, but was quite sure that she would soon be well. The doctor had told him that now the baby had been born Mother would be rid of all her complications.

When the two of us got home Father gave me all sorts of good things to eat and kept telling me what a fine big baby brother I had now. With a pang of jealousy I realized that Father was more proud of him and liked him better than he liked me.

Next day another sister of Mother's arrived all the way from Helsinki. She looked just as young as Mother, but she was taller and she carried herself better. Her clothes were so elegant that I couldn't get used to her, though she promised now to look after me until Mother was well enough to come home. Every day she dressed me in my best clothes and took me with her to lots of shops downtown to buy this and that. When we got home she would lie down on the bed and find

73

all kinds of things for me to do. In particular, I remember that we took a lot of newspapers at that time, whatever they were, and my chief task was to carry them one at a time from room to room. When the whole bundle had been moved from the kitchen to the parlor, I had to start moving them back from the parlor to the kitchen, and then back again. I was not often allowed out, as I was told I would get myself and my best clothes dirty.

I wonder how long those disturbed and anxious days lasted? Sometimes when Father came home he was happy and proud and told us a lot about his new son. But at other times he too was restless and worried just as I was. I realize now that my brother's birth had made Mother very ill, but at that time I imagined it was all my brother's fault and I almost began to hate him before I had even seen him. It was he who had taken Mother away from me, pushed me out of Father's mind, and turned my whole world upside down.

Every day I kept asking and asking when Mother and my little brother were coming home. I had vague hopes that as soon as Mother saw me she would forget that other one, and hug me and kiss me as she had always done. Then the new boy would have to keep out of the way and just watch us, and perhaps even Father would notice that it was me they must think of first.

Then one day Mother did come home, but her homecoming was quite different from what I had imagined. A horse cab suddenly pulled up in front of our steps, my aunt rushed out, snatched a white bundle with some invisible object inside it from my father's arms and began to bring it inside. Father took hold of Mother, who was sitting beside him—a very strange-looking, pale, thin, and wrinkled mother—helped her down and then supported her up the steps. When they got inside, Mother looked at me, smiled wanly, and put a tired hand on my head. Without saying a word she went straight into the front room with Father.

That same evening I was allowed to see my brother. When Mother had been safely put to bed and the bundle set down beside her, I was taken in to see her. When the baby began crying with his shrill voice, he was given a small nursing bottle, which he grabbed greedily. Because of Mother's illness he had to accustom himself to cow's milk right from the start, unlike me earlier and the ones who came after him, but it didn't seem to bother him. As soon as I saw his red, wrinkled face, his thick head of hair and chubby hands, I had a feeling that, small as he was, his strength was greater than mine. When the bottle slipped from his mouth, he opened his eyes angrily, let out a lusty howl, and grabbed anything that came in the way of his thrashing arms.

"Isn't he adorable!" my fashionable aunt kept exclaiming. "He's certainly a wonderfully fine, sturdy lad!"

Mother and Father smiled happily, looking now at each other, now at their younger son. They had almost forgotten my existence.

When he grew up, this boy became a very good athlete and was for many years a champion diver. When war broke out, he was killed the first time he went into action. A piece of shrapnel ripped his chest open, but he battled for his life many hours before death claimed him.

But I must keep to my childhood.

Next day Mother's sister went back to Helsinki and in her place came an old woman with her small grandson. Life gradually got back to normal. I was well fed, I had a nice playmate and so I enjoyed being outside. We spent most of our time in the yard, where it was highest, building all sorts of things. But once or twice he took me home with him, right to the other side of the town, where I came to know the strong smell of the cellulose works and saw its chimneys reaching far into the sky. There was never anyone at home, as both his parents were at work in the daytime, so we didn't stay there either. It was just that my playmate got homesick now and then and we would run and have a look at it, but having seen it we hurried back to my place.

As soon as we got inside, I would rush straight into the other room, and life felt more and more secure. Usually my brother was asleep in the basket placed beside Mother, and she would smile at me and begin to talk to me more and more. Her face lost its whiteness and thin wrinkles and in other ways too she began to look herself again.

But it was only in the evenings when Father came home that I really began to get used to my brother. As a rule we all shut ourselves in the inner room, as the old woman who was looking after us occupied the kitchen with the little boy. Mother would even sit up, her back propped against a pile of pillows, and start combing her hair. Father had also moved his rocking chair in here and would sit rocking in his quiet way. Only when the baby despot awoke and began to cry was there anything of a stir. But when he had been fed or washed and changed into clean, tightly wrapped cloths, he fell asleep again, and peace and quiet surrounded us once more. At a time like this I would often go up to my brother, gaze at him searchingly, and be inclined to agree that perhaps he was a more important member of the family than I was. And at the same time I began in one way to love him and feel as proud of him as Mother and Father did.

One day Mother got up for the first time and took a few turns up and down the room, tottering but smiling happily. From then on she got well quickly, walking up and down the room for longer at a stretch, and doing all kinds of odd jobs. After that it was not long before the old woman and her grandson went out of my life. I did not miss them particularly, not even the boy. It had been fun playing about outside with him, but it meant much more to me that we now had our home all to ourselves.

76

CHAPTER THREE

1

Father's income at this time must have been less; at any rate Mother began to insist on our finding a cheaper place to live. Father seemed to take this to heart, but one day—about a year after the birth of my brother—we moved with our belongings into the middle of town, to a cheap and old-fashioned building in the yard of a dignified house next to the police station. Our new home consisted of one small room which we reached by going through the laundry room and bakery.

Perhaps it was so unpleasant living in such a place that from the start my memory lowered a thick veil over all that happened. I can mention many different things, but I cannot bring any of them to life. From near this house I saw the first stagecoach, drawn by two horses, set off for Hovinsaari; it tempted people living far from the center of town with a comfortable and cheap ride home, but old-fashioned people did not understand such new-fangled things and laughed the attempt to scorn. Here I earned money for the first time, when our landlady, an elegant Swedish-speaking woman, paid us small boys to stack a large pile of firewood into the shed for the winter. Unfortunately we were not yet very strong and would not have finished by nightfall if my father had not helped us when he got home from work. While in this house I once ate so many bananas that I kept throwing up all night and they became so repulsive to me that not until I was a grown man did I dare to put one in my mouth. In this house I saw for the first time the rapturous beginning and the dismal end of love. The landlady had a plump servant who did the washing for two days in the laundry room in front of our room, and almost the whole time she was visited by a handsome young man. Every time I ran through the laundry room on my way out or in, I saw the girl sitting in the man's arms in an ecstasy of passionate and never-ending kisses. After we had moved from there I heard that a fatherless child had been born to an out-of-work mother who was driven to misery and destitution. In this house, too, I came to know the dreaded police and the important and respected town doctor on the other side of the street.

I could mention many things that were new to me, but I can describe none of them in detail. Everything is vague and blurry, sunk into oblivion. After about a year, when we moved again to another, more comfortable place, my memory begins once more to clear.

To my mind I was quite a big boy when I moved to this new place. I no longer bothered much about Father and Mother, as long as I was fed. I spent more of my time out of doors. My younger brother was not dressed in white petti-coats any more, but in short trousers and a shirt just as I was in the summer.

The house to which we now moved was close to the woods, to the old ramparts, and to a large meadow enclosed by thick birch trees. Beneath our window ran the same road along which I had gone with Father the first time I went swimming. But now I saw everything with different eyes. New houses had been built around us and our yard was very wide. Where we were, there were four houses, one of which was a two-story brick house containing, besides living premises, two saunas, a bakehouse, and a laundry room. The outhouses, pigsties, and storage sheds were also big. Everything was large and solid.

Here, too, we had only one room to live in, but it was more comfortable than the previous one. There were many grown-ups and many children all around us. From the hall four doors opened straight into four homes; the windows of two rooms opened onto the street and those of the other two onto the yard. Under each room was a large cellar, where, during the winter, there was space for little else but firewood; in the summer almost all the food and the kegs of homemade beer were kept there as well.

It was here that I got to know my pock-marked aunt's eldest daughter. I had not seen her for a long time. Now she was a sweet, pretty young wife of eighteen expecting her second child. She and her husband lived in two rooms of an older house next door, and every day she would ask me to come in and see her. She loved all small children.

At the same time I got to know her husband, and began to like him even better than his wife. He was the son of the rich sawmill owner and his proud wife. His parents also owned this block of houses with their saunas; but as they felt he had been foolish and disobedient, he had been taken away from school and had become a sauna stoker.

It had been a blow to this spirited and virile young man to be separated from educated people and thrown amongst workmen. But in my eyes at least he seemed happy and contented. As soon as I was awake in the mornings and had drunk my coffee and eaten my bread and butter, I would rush out and go straight to him. Usually he cleaned out the refuse pit in front of his workshop first and put the rubbish under the outhouse. Then he would clean the boilers and begin to cart firewood from the shed to the boiler room. I thought this was exciting. The boiler room was about six feet above ground, and a long, sloping gangplank had been made into it from the side of the steps so that the barrows of wood could be easily rolled in. As he wheeled the load up at a gay, youthful run, I would trot happily behind. To my even greater joy, when the empty barrow had been turned round, I was lifted in and became its load, and away we went at a dizzy speed. The planks creaked and sagged under the bounding barrow and the air sang merrily in my ears. These rides were a great experience, as they produced in me both a chilling fear and a courage which developed my strength and widened my knowledge. I felt that with the help of these experiences I was really growing up to be a man.

When enough wood had been carted the young stoker would light the boiler and then go to see how the saunas were getting on and if the pipes were in order. Downstairs were the men's and women's public saunas, upstairs the gentlefolk's private sauna. The men's public sauna was the only one I knew; I was taken there at intervals to be bathed.

In addition to the young married couple and the sauna, I gradually became acquainted with the whole block of houses and the people living in them. I still remember very well what they all looked like, though most of them are dead by now and I can recall the names of only a few. I also have a clear picture of some of my playmates from that time, though I have lost touch with them since then.

There were always a lot of children in the yard, girls and boys, big and small. My younger brother was among them, but I only joined them when I was tired of the sauna and the young mother. The boys of my size formed a group of their own which often went off exploring the more exciting nooks and crannies. All the others would lose sight of us as we climbed onto roofs and into attics, poking about amidst the lumber and junk hoarded up in corners. When at last we came back to the others, we were always black from head to foot and made our mothers angry or sometimes even cry.

Another interesting place was behind the sauna's storage shed, where this building narrowed into a cluster of sheds and outhouses belonging to the families who lived on the other side of the sauna. In front of these doors was a level plank bridge about three feet high which you could reach only by the steps at the end. Since an old water barrel had been left lying on the bridge, it was quite a dizzy jump from the top. At first only the biggest boys dared to jump off; but as the ground underneath was black soil it soon grew soft and then the smaller boys too were bold enough to try.

Behind our outhouses ran a solid fence about six feet high, and a few yards on the other side were our neighbors' outhouses. The paths on both sides of the fence were very smelly and overgrown with long nettles, so it was not very nice to walk there. But it was fun to climb over the fence, and as the girls and smallest boys did not dare to follow us, we would vanish from sight and had to breathe the pungent air of these strange back ways.

I did not get to know the people in the yards next door this summer. There were two smaller yards adjoining our big wide one; in one of these there were nothing but grownups and old people and in the other only one boy. In the block on the other side of the street there were several other children; the bigger boys would sometimes stop to talk or play with them, but those of my size looked askance at them. They were strangers and perhaps enemies as well. Not until later, when we were a little bigger, did we get to know them better.

As a rule we kept to our own yard, except on hot days, when we ran to the beach along the same road down which Mother and Father had taken me to swim for the first time. Now, however, we did not go right to the point or stop at the warm, shallow bay, but ran across the point to the other beach. The bay there was wide, and between the islands in the distance we saw the sea join the sky somewhere very far away. The water was chilly and clear, although the town sewage flowed into it nearby, and between the heavy boulders the bottom was covered with coarse but smooth sand. It was a good spot to splash about in. From the top of a steep rock a little way out from the shore I learned to dive head first, though I could not yet swim and the water reached only to my chest.

It was in this house and among these people that I got ready for going to school. Before this phase of my life began another brother was born, a strong, healthy boy who grew quickly. But I also saw death at close quarters, and it was violent and dramatic. My aunt's daughter was just about to give birth to her second child when her husband and my gay hero fell ill one day with brain fever. For two days he sweated and tossed, unconscious, and as the moment of death drew near his wife's cries of pain filled the whole yard. The moment he was buried the rest of his family too seemed to be wiped from the face of the earth. The eldest child was sent away to one of their wealthy relations, and when the young mother began to recover from her agony the newly-born baby was taken away to another family. The mother was sent to Helsinki to be trained as a nurse. By the time I started going to school, they were nothing but a memory.

One day Mother dressed me in my best clothes and set off in good time to take me to school. The doors were still shut and so everyone collected in the yard. Most of the other boys and girls also had their mothers with them, and a few had their fathers or big sisters. There were all kinds of children among them. Some had already begun their rough games even here, but the very shy ones kept close beside their mothers, holding them tightly by the hand. Between these extreme types there was of course every possible other kind.

When the janitor opened the doors we began to file slowly inside. The teachers had had a lot of tables brought into the big gymnasium, and we stood in front of them beside our mothers, sisters, and fathers. Although all that happened was that our parents handed over our birth certificates and said our names, there was something solemn about the moment. Even the very wild boys who had been playing roughly in the yard were silent. Teachers inspired great respect, but at the same time we seemed to be aware of something else. Perhaps that our life as it had been up to now was finished and a new phase was beginning.

After this I always ran to school alone. There were so many of us newcomers that we were divided into two big classes. My class was put into a smaller building next door, and at the other end of this building were the Swedish-speaking children. I heard their voices so often, both indoors and out in the yard, that I felt I was closer to them than the older pupils in the big building.

I remember that my teacher was young, very pretty and very well dressed. Almost every morning she appeared in a new dress, sometimes in two different dresses on the same day. She tried to be a stern teacher, and her sharp exclamations often made the more sensitive ones tremble and turn pale with fear, but the very rough boys only grinned and laughed. Although they were made to stand in the corner time and again, they could not take things seriously. The teacher herself was much more serious, as at least once she burst into tears when she saw that her strictness was in vain.

Learning to read and write was easy for me, and so these lessons were pleasant. I held up my hand eagerly the whole time, but after two or three tests my reading was not listened to any more. In the writing class I always had my lessons done in a flash and then I spent the time watching gleefully how hard the poorer students had to work. The teacher was not satisfied with me all the same. I could write the letters and words quite correctly, but my handwriting was appalling. All the years I was at school it remained almost as bad.

As more subjects were added and we began to learn drawing, handicraft, and singing, I knew moments of crushing depression. If I felt proud of myself during reading and writing lessons, I wanted to sink through the floor with shame during these other lessons. From the very first I had to admit that I was being left behind by nearly all the others. I sweated and strained, sweated and strained, but however hard I tried I could never get anything finished. Time and again the teacher would stop beside my desk during drawing and handicraft lessons and begin to help me by guiding my hand while all the others watched inquisitively. I went red in the face over and over again, and when the teacher left me I was always so upset that I would smudge the drawing she had helped me with or hopelessly tangle the potholder she had begun.

In singing I would make sounds with the others until the teacher made us sing one by one. At first I tried this too several times, but I soon found that my singing was just as bad as my drawing and knitting and I kept quiet. In this

84

subject nothing was expected of me at all. On my report card there was one long stroke instead of a number.

I had a wonderfully happy time the first two winters in the school playground during recess. Nearly every day we boys played what we called "threes." The walls of the school building and the janitor's lodge opposite were starting points. We began the game by placing one boy in the middle of the playground to catch the rest of us with three strokes. As we were a big team when we started off, this lone boy could usually seize two or three during the very first run and win them over to his side with three strokes. When we started on the second run from the opposite wall our team was thus smaller and the number of catchers had increased and strengthened so that in this run we lost heavily. After several more runs the greater part of the team had been transferred to the middle of the field and the only runners left were one or two very fast and tough players. Only then did the really glorious struggle begin.

The big group of boys in the middle of the field usually picked off one victim at a time from the last runners. He was surrounded, seized by his shirt, trousers, hands, and legs, so that he was forced to give in. In this way one after the other of the best men were overcome and taken over to the other side.

I was among these, and gradually I became the best of them all, the last one left and almost unbeatable. I was not the strongest, but I was swift and unscrupulously tough. I could feel some inner joy filling my whole body and making me attack my would-be capturers despite the odds.

How happy I was! How brave, how daring, how superior to all the others!

When I started running I always headed straight for the middle, the most threatening and frightening center of danger. But when I got up to the others and they tried to throw a ring round me, I dodged suddenly and slipped between their fingers. The only opponents left in my way were one or two timid souls who kept apart from the others, and they were easily crushed. I simply charged straight at them and they fled out of my way in panic, and the road was open to the wall of the other building.

I did not win every time of course. Strong hands would seize my shirt, arms, or legs, and then my game was up and I had to begin the next game as a catcher. But it did not often happen on my good days. Much more often I raced time and again past the boys of our class or straight through them and kept my first game going until the school bell put an end to it. These victories of mine came to be the most wonderful victories of my childhood. I grew high in the regard of the boys of our class, and of the girls too.

They were the first and last victories of my life.

I myself could not then grasp—nor can I even now—what my success was based on. I can guess up to a point, but it is always a mystery how I could behave so wildly in the school yard, while in class I was usually a good boy, and out of school probably more of a coward than a hero. Fights, at least, I really dreaded and I kept out of them.

When school was over we had to carry our slates with us, as well as our books, and they broke easily. For this reason they were a great nuisance to us, for when we had broken the slates given us by the school our parents had to pay for all the others, and naturally they did not like it a bit. On the contrary, in their anger they were quite liable to seize the birch or some other means of punishment. But in spite of this, the slates got broken time and again—in a fight, if we fell when running, or if we bumped into something. Boys cannot always be so quiet on the way home that they don't knock their things about.

86

Homework always seemed easy, as long as I had to write only words and simple sums on the slate. But sometimes a drawing was assigned as homework and this banished nearly all my peace of mind. On such days I had to sit inside for many hours, drawing and rubbing out, sweating and sometimes even crying. My parents could not understand why I took my homework so seriously, but deep inside me was the stern requirement that the drawing of an apple must really look like an apple, and berries must really look like berries, and when I was not equal to this I was in despair. At home these lessons for some reason seemed more important than at school, perhaps partly because the drawings done at school were wiped out straight away, but those done at home had to be carried through the town and many of the people I met often wanted to look at them. But what seemed even more important was that in this very homework my ego was really beginning to be awakened and to find out its limitations and capabilities.

Fortunately such homelessons were rare. When I had taken my things home and got something to eat, I would usually forget about school and would rush out in search of new adventure.

III

I first made the acquaintance of Christmas when I was ill, and I began then to honor it. When I was in the second grade at school it again drew near to me, but in quite a new way. Before the somber shadows began to fall over all our family it wanted once more to remind me of itself, to lift my spirit to heaven and to leave in my mind the memory of a phase of my life that was soon to close.

I noticed the approach of this Christmas when our class began in good time to learn Christmas songs, first in our own classroom and a little later together with another class in the gymnasium. Although, being a poor singer, I dared to do no more than hum with the others, something of the meaning of these songs flowed into me right from the beginning, bringing with it something quite new, startling, and arresting. Just what was it I experienced? I soon realized that it was something very solemn, but that was not enough. I was meeting things of which previously I had not even been aware.

And when, after a time, round dances were added to our community singing, my spirits rose still higher. In the round dances each boy had to take a girl by the hands. Every time this happened I gave a start. I became excruciatingly shy. I blushed. I did not dare to look at my partner or anyone else, and my whole body almost perspired from the strange excitement. But even so I enjoyed these times. I noticed that the girls whose hands were linked in mine did not look at me either, but gave themselves up with their entire being to the joy of singing and dancing. The plain notes of the harmonium, the equally simple words of the songs, and the touch of our hands all tended to raise me to some unknown state of being.

Christmas seemed to take on an entirely new meaning. The words of the songs spoke of games and of the outward happenings of games, and in their more solemn moments the teachers spoke of the candles soon to be lighted and of the birth of Jesus. But of the secret sources of our joy they said nothing. Perhaps the grownups had already forgotten all about them.

On other days this mood was also with me at recess and followed me home from school. On such days I did not go with the crowd of other boys, but kept to myself. Not even my great victories during recess attracted me. I felt that the inexplicable moods awaking within me were of a fragile stuff which would easily break if a stranger were to brush against it. They belonged to me alone, and the more carefully I was able to hide them from others the more precious they would be. Not even the girls whose hands I held as I floated away on the music and the songs from the circle of everyday things meant anything to me apart from the games. Sometimes I might stop to look at them from a distance, but withdrawn into their own sphere they were merely girls, whom boys always despised.

I sensed that I myself was in the process of changing.

Even on those days when the songs and games were forgotten and I went on as before with my lessons and threw myself with gusto into the battles in the playground, someone might suddenly touch me and make me think of something. The teacher would look at me in wonder and call me by name. In the midst of my wild running I would sometimes suddenly stop so that my playmates nearly crushed me beneath them in their joy. But at such moments these things meant nothing to me. I answered the teacher's questions clearly and plainly, and I submitted in silence to my playmates' enthusiastic chatter.

The nearer our festival approached the more excited I became and the more eagerly my imagination went to work. All the days were lovely and full of wonder. I came to know the sunshine and the dark beauty of heavy showers of rain, of the cold sea winds, and the late autumn evenings. They were always full of things and events which the gaily bubbling stream of thought brought with it. The nights were sometimes restless. I did not dream; but I tossed excitedly in my bed, often talking aloud at great length and occasionally uttering inexplainable cries which woke Mother and made her wake me with her frightened questioning. I could not tell her anything, nor could I understand why she had awakened me.

89

Once awake, I was quite calm. When Mother had tucked me in again, I quickly fell asleep and resumed my unknown struggles.

On the day of the festival, Mother dressed me in new clothes and set off with me to school. A large crowd of grownups had again collected in the playground, just as when we came the first time. But now none of my pals stayed beside their parents. They formed groups of their own. I kept to myself, also apart from my mother. It was as if I had to muster my forces for what lay ahead. When the bell rang we assembled as usual in our lines and marched into class. There the teachers made short speeches to us and reminded us how we were to behave. More subdued than usual, we entered the gymnasium, and our parents sat down on benches placed in rows or stood about against the wall. We marched in front, in full view of them all. At that moment I felt the spirit of the festival encircling us and making my steps as light as the wing-beats of a bird.

The event itself is hard to describe. When the harmonium began to play and the girls' and boys' voices were raised in song around me, I kept quiet to hear more plainly what the devout voices were singing and to understand what they had to tell. I was aware of the whir of angels' wings close at hand and I saw faces surrounded by a perpetual light. Every evening outside I had seen man-made lights which were always accompanied by a dark shadow; but in this light there were no shadows. It was full of brightness.

"Never believe in evil, believe always in good," I said quietly to myself in my own childish words.

When I glanced at my mother, I saw her eyes radiant with happiness and tears. She too at this moment believed as I did.

When the hymn was finished the teacher told us a fairy tale. Its name has gone from me nor can I say now what it was about, except that it suddenly took us away from our school hall and our town to somewhere very far away in the midst of the Finnish forests. Dazzling white snowdrifts covered the ground, and the boundless forest slumbered its winter sleep, garbed in white hoarfrost beneath the glittering stars. Its white mantle protected even a small tumbledown cottage where poor people lived. A snowdrift crept right up to the window and a thick drift on the roof hung down over the eaves. A yellow gleam through the tiny frosted window and a narrow path trodden through the snow to the door were the only signs that people lived there. Everywhere that evening whiteness surrounded it.

Always believe in good, never believe in evil. Always see beauty, never see ugliness.

That evening these people were hungry, for they had nothing to eat; but as they too believed in goodness and beauty and not in evil and ugliness, Father Christmas himself brought them a big pile of Christmas presents and all kinds of good things to eat. And I believed that this happened. I was in the midst of the Finnish forests and I saw it with my own eyes.

All the girls and boys sang more fervently than ever before, and I heard that their words were full of a new, inexplicable emotion and joy. Even in poverty there was no evil or ugliness. I was certain of it. And it was proved to me in yet another way. When the singing was over, presents were handed out to us too, a small paper bag to each, and when I opened it and took a bite of the apple inside, I felt goodness and beauty on my tongue.

But all this was only the preparation for more important things. Up to now I had been merely a listener and a looker-on, but when the round games began I really took part in what was happening. The singing and the fairy tale had floated high above us; now goodness and beauty stepped down into our midst. The words of new sings began to live within me, and when I grasped a girl's hand I was no longer alone. I was part of the universe from which goodness and beauty stream and where the light is free of shadows.

Those around me were singing. I heard their words and voices. I did not take part in the singing and I did not dare to look at the face of the girl whose hand I was holding, but all my limbs tingled and floated still higher, up, up.

Always believe in goodness, never believe in evil. See always beauty, never see ugliness. Never be alone.

The girls' hands were so small and soft that they felt as if they might break into nothingness if I squeezed hard. But it was through their hands that good poured into me and with the help of their hands I could float still higher and yet at the same time be on the earth, in this gymnasium and inside my own self.

When I hear children singing their round games nowadays they seem familiar. The words of some are quite the same as during my schooldays; but at the same time they are strangely commonplace. They do not kindle faith; they do not speak of the mysteries that uplifted us then.

That day I had to take many girls by the hand as many kinds of tunes and words floated round me, and I was aware how different all the hands were. Some were like red or white flowers, others again were so delicate that one could have blown them into space like the white fluff of a dandelion, and some were so small that one could only find them by looking under the green leaves.

Never be alone.

These words rang in my head as the teacher at last spoke to us again of Christmas and the Christmas holidays and as the last song was begun. They were still ringing in my head as, tired now, I walked through the streets holding Mother's hand. It was freezing outside and the low-lying clouds were dark gray, but the words were ringing in my head even so, and I told myself that I would always believe in goodness and beauty and that I would never be alone.

IV

After that day I tried with all my strength to keep on believing, but right from the first it was very hard. The brightness quickly began to fade.

When Christmas came to our own little home, Father gave me some small skis which he had carved from board ends; they were tarred and scorched underneath to make them glide, and both I and my younger brother got guns all the way from Helsinki with which you could shoot peas and paper balls. The very same day, Christmas Eve, I felt I must go into the yard to try out my skis and shoot my gun. Time and again I tried to say to myself the words that had made me happy on that other evening and had seemed so easy to understand, but now they made me restless. I could not keep still. My uneasiness was more easily forgotten when I fired the gun.

I spent every day of the holidays skiing down the slope in our yard and even went outside the yard where the slopes were steeper. I was on the move from morning till night. If I tired of skiing, I would fetch my gun and begin shooting it off, with all the boys in our yard crowding round. They pretended to despise it, but I could see from their eyes that they envied me and I would bang away harder than ever. My younger brother was still so small that his gun was hung up on a nail, but I was free to fire mine as much as I liked. And I fired it often. I had to hear those bangs to forget something else.

The whole winter became almost a winter of waiting. When I got to school I would sit very quietly in class and fasten all my attention on the lesson, and at recess I continued my successful running in our wild games. But a kind of vacuum surrounded me. I had no sense of satisfaction or peace of mind.

Sometimes I would go and stand by myself in a corner of the playground to recollect something and to look from afar at the girls. But these attempts felt so oddly stupid that I had to run back quickly into the crowd of boys.

I was then eight years old.

When the cold became so severe that skiing down the slope was out of the question, and when my gun was suddenly broken, I often used to stare from the top of our steps at the apartment in the house next door where the young mother had always been so pleased to see me. But now a very old married couple, whose children were grown up, lived there. On such days when it was freezing hard I used to long for the family that had suddenly disappeared, though otherwise I had almost forgotten them. At home I felt quite alone.

Eventually I intruded on another family. Their father was dead, and the mother's unmarried sister had come to live with them. There were three children, two of them girls, and the younger of the girls was in my class at school. We had not gotten to know each other very well at school, but here at home I hoped I could see her at close quarters and hear what she had to say.

In their home no one kept quiet for a second. In the summer the women worked down at the harbor; but as the port was icebound in the winter they made a living by doing handwork of different kinds. They knitted socks and mittens, patched workmen's clothes, and cut worn-out clothes into narrow strips to be woven into rugs. The side of room near the window was full of skeins of yarn and piles of clothing. The children, on the other hand, always romped round the stove. They cried and squabbled, chewed bread and drank water, climbed onto the stove to get warm, or hid from each other under the bed. I thought all this was very interesting, but it

94

became still more interesting when the girls sometimes had to do their homework. The first few times I actually gave a start when I heard them reading aloud. The younger of them did just the same homework as I did, but it seemed peculiar all the same. The words dropped from her lips like bits of wood, and when I asked her afterwards what she had read she could not tell me. Even the elder sister, who could read fluently and who had longer lessons, was quite unable to say what her books were all about.

When I was with them I grew more restless than ever, but nevertheless I began to go there more and more often. I expected that I would gradually understand something that was difficult to comprehend. I expected to learn something which I did not yet understand.

Mother, however, was of a different mind. On my way out from a visit one day, I met Mother with the slop pail in her hand, and she began to question me about where I had been. When I explained, she seized my hand and took me inside. And there she threatened me with dire punishment if I did not keep away from these people. In her opinion they earned their bread not only by honest work, but also in some dreadful and sinful way. In addition, the children's mother was thought to have a dangerous, contagious disease in her nose.

Of course I had already noticed that the woman's nose was bandaged with a white rag, but I had never given it a thought. Wounds were to be seen almost every day, either on one's own body or somebody else's. But now my curiosity was awakened. Although Mother had forbidden me, I slipped into our neighbors' when she was not looking, my mind full of excited anticipation. I almost thought that now I would find what I had been forced to go in search of.

Perhaps I was forced to search for the shadow that is behind all living beings and behind all things.

As I entered the room, I was met by a smell quite

different from the one in my own home. I immediately recognized the smell exuding from the pile of old clothes and I was also aware that neither the grownups' nor the children's clothes, nor the floor, had been washed nearly as often as at home, so that there was a peculiar smell from these too. But there was still something else hidden in the smell, something just as pungent as the smell of lysol, but different. I stared at the mother's nose swathed in its white bandage and I went as close as possible to her. But the strong odor was not coming from there. To my disappointment the nose smelled quite clean, as a clean bandage was put on every day.

The women were sitting facing each other at the window with their backs bent, cutting strips of carpet-rag. From the musty pile they snatched now a man's shirt or pair of trousers, now a woman's skirt or underclothes, and let their scissors fly along them at the most amazing rate. The bundles had arrived from somewhere in the middle of town and were returned there rolled up into round balls. And the cutters were in such a hurry that they hardly had time to glance at me.

"Believe in good. Don't believe in evil," I said silently to myself as I watched them.

But the queer smell clung to my nostrils and the people and the floor were not so well washed as at home. I could see them now quite clearly in the light of my mother's prohibition, and I could feel no belief in goodness.

I sat down near the stove and kept quite still. I listened to the girls shouting and squabbling or to the way the words read aloud fell out so oddly, almost unintelligibly, and I watched the girls chewing bread and drinking water and climbing onto the stove to get warm. I sensed that the smell and the dirt had brought me nearer to something, but the full understanding of what it might be was still hidden from me.

I went there many many times, but I got no further and I found no peace. Our relationship came to an end in an

96

extraordinary way. One day their small boy, who was not yet going to school, had been given a ten *penni* bit, an unusually large coin. He was standing in the yard with the money in his hand and showing it to anyone who cared to look. When asked where he had got it, he said that he had got it from a strange man. The thought came to me that I was close to that second part of my mother's explanation of why I should keep away from them, close to those awful things which also helped them to live. Perhaps I would begin to understand if I could hold that coin in my hand.

The boy, however, would not agree to this. It could be looked at, but only in his hand. No one might even touch it.

Then it seemed as if I really must hold that money in my hand to find out what it would tell me, what it would explain to me. Suddenly grabbing his hand, I forced open the fist which he instinctively clenched and, despite his frightened screams, seized the money and began to run. I ran about a dozen yards or so, followed by the shouts of the boys and even a woman, before I threw the money down in disappointment, vanished into the other yard, and climbed up into the attic of the next house.

But, there, when I was quite alone, I began to feel that I had touched something terrible. It had dirtied and disgraced me. I no longer dared to say "Believe in goodness." I had become bad myself. For a long time I kept spitting my mouth dry, so that at least a little of my wickedness would leave me.

A large crowd of women had collected in the yard round the crying boy, gesturing and talking excitedly about what had happened. They were all amazed. No one had thought me a thief before, but now they must believe it. Now they must be careful where I was concerned and keep their children away from me. Among the poor there was no one more dangerous than a thief.

I felt that a black shadow was spreading round me and

97

making me still more alone. Through the cracks in the attic I could see all that was going on in the yard and hear all that was being said. When the women began to lead the crying boy home consolingly, I slipped down from the attic to the yard and ran back to where I had thrown the money. It was still there. Without touching it, I called to the boy to come and get it.

He approached doubtfully, followed by the women and the other boys. And they all saw that the money had been near them all the time.

"I thought all along that he was no thief," one of the women exclaimed. "He was only teasing that other boy."

But all were not of the same mind. They had drawn their conclusions and were unwilling to abandon them.

"He's a thief all right. He threw it away because he was scared."

What the women said did not worry me at all. I was thinking of what I had gone through and I knew quite well that the boys' opinion of me was quite different from that of their mothers. That day they kept away from me, but next day only a few remembered about it, and very soon they let me play with them again.

When Mother heard about it she punished me more severely than ever before, but that did not worry me either. Not even my smarting backside bothered me. At that moment I had far more important matters to think of, so that things like that meant nothing to me. I rather dreaded Father's homecoming, but when Mother told him what I had done he only looked at me for longer than usual in silence. As I stared into his eyes I thought I saw that he was recollecting his own far-off boyhood.

Once more I spent all my spare time on the ski slope, and when the thaw set in I went over to the yard on the other side of the street. I dared now to join those boys as well. That winter snowball fights were started which lasted for many years, and as I gradually got more skillful in the art I began to like these snowfights better than skiing. In them I could forget myself for long periods at a stretch.

v

Summer came, and one day Mother received an urgent message from Father's place of work: "Your husband has been taken ill. Come at once." The messenger, an old woman, added that Mother had better run first to the druggist to buy some "stroke drops," as Father was paralyzed.

Quickly throwing a kerchief round her head, Mother told me in an anxious voice to look after my two small brothers while she was away. Before this there had been no need for me to bother about them and I had no idea how they spent their time. But now I took charge of them instinctively and they, frightened, clung to me. Mother was away for some hours. We went out into the yard once or twice, but quickly came inside again. We could not really comprehend what had happened to Father, but we knew from Mother's face and her tone of voice that something alarming and perhaps really dreadful had happened to him. So we could do nothing but wait until she came back.

It was evening before Mother got home. She cried and hugged us by turns. Then she made us some coffee and sandwiches. Apparently she meant to keep us out of it and bear her sorrow alone. But when I asked where Father was, why he had not come home as usual, she burst out crying again. "Father will be away for a long time now," she said. "Father is very, very ill."

When I had gone to bed, I dared to repeat again after a

long time the words which once had made me happy. Now, however, I longed not for happiness, but for strength, and it seemed that they gave it to me.

Only later did I find out what had happened to Father. During the morning he had trimmed the basic stonework of a building as usual. In the afternoon he had felt ill, but had gone stubbornly on with his work until another stonemason stopped beside him in amazement.

"What's the idea," he exclaimed. "You've gone and spoiled the whole stone!"

Father stopped working, looked at his comrade, tried to say something, but could not get a word out. Then he slowly collapsed in a huddle.

It now dawned on the man what was wrong and he called to the others. They all saw that Father had cut the stone crookedly, and that he could neither speak nor stand up. But he was still half-conscious. An old woman was asked to go and tell Mother, as none of the workmen had time.

Thanks to this woman, Mother hurried first to the druggist to buy drops before running to Father's place of work. When she got there with the drops, Father was unconscious. He was just being lifted onto a stone-cart to be taken to the little hospital. All Mother could do was to go along with the load, crying. At the hospital she helped the nurse to undress Father and put him to bed.

After some time I too got to know this ward. I went there with Mother the first time when Father could already sit up on a stool beside the bed. After that, I went many times alone to take him coffee. There were some six or eight beds in the ward and one of the other men would always be sitting on his stool telling yarns. The others lay in bed, either battling with fever, their glowing eyes wide open, or wandering restlessly in the realm of sleep. But one did not bother much about them. No one could help them, and each sooner or later had to walk the sharp road of pain or set off on his last journey. These were things beyond human knowledge, and it was best to keep within the sphere of this known world as long as possible.

Father was the same quiet man here as at home and only took part in the conversation as a listener. Quite often he would smile, now and then as though transfigured. He smiled at the men's talk; they talked to keep their spirits up and to hide their individual secrets. But Father smiled at something else as well, at those mute visions of his which even as a very small boy I had seen from the rocking chair.

I was always aware of it when I entered this room without Mother. Father would take the coffee bottle eagerly and begin to drink from it and to ask how things were at home. At the same time he would look at me with his bright eyes, laying his hand on my head or shoulder now and then almost as a caress. Something light and uplifting flowed into my being. I felt at these moments that I was floating above the everyday world.

My former uneasiness had changed to another. The shadows were darkening around me. Nevertheless, at these moments, I dared to believe in good.

At home our spirits were subdued and depressed. I heard that Mother had had to take our small savings out of the bank, and now and then I noticed that she was crying, although she tried not to let us see. My young brothers too were uneasy for a time, but they soon adjusted themselves to our changed condition and began to play as before.

I tried to do the same. I became aware more keenly than ever of the loveliness and freedom of the summer. My playmates went farther afield and spent longer times by the sea than the previous summer. I went with them. I came to know new parts of the woods, new hills, and a long "canal" that had fallen into decay, a relic of the town's past. There were other places too, like the tumbledown old ramparts, now conquered by the roots of trees that had grown into a forest. I helped the other boys to find birds' nests of different kinds. Some were high up on the branches of trees or in cavities in the trunks; others were on the ground under stones or in the banks of ditches. On these excursions my eyes and ears took in all kinds of new things. When we went swimming we would go more and more often to the town's swimming-baths among the grownups. There I learned to swim properly, doing the breast stroke like all the best swimmers, although I still kept in the shallow part where I could touch bottom if necessary.

But all this time I did not forget Father. I knew peace and I knew shadow. I remembered them even at moments when I encountered something exciting or instructive. Very many times the shadow swept over me so violently that I had to drop everything and run home as fast as I could. I only calmed down when I saw Mother and could tell from her face that nothing new had happened.

What can Mother's feelings have been? At first she tried to go on with her life as before, but there was not enough for her to do now. Father did not need food or to have his working clothes washed and mended. Mother no longer took pleasure in keeping the room spotlessly clean. As there were always a few women sunning themselves or gossiping in the yard, Mother would often join them. But I suppose she was prey to the same restlessness as I was, for she could not stay long in any one place.

As the weeks passed another frightening thing began to threaten us—hunger. The money gave out and no more came in. This really roused Mother. One day she went into town to hear about work, and as she had been in service with rich families as a young girl, she went to one of them first of all. And she did not have to go any further. A few days previously an old washerwoman had been taken to the same hospital as Father and her place was vacant. Mother was asked to start work the following day with the first family.

Next morning I had to wake up early, though I was still heavy-eyed with sleep. Mother was already dressed and the coffee was made, and when I had had a cup and felt more awake, she began to give me instructions. When the younger children woke up, I was to give them coffee and sandwiches. The pot would keep hot on the stove for another hour or two. Then I was to stay with them all day, so that they would not get lost or into mischief. And if we felt hungry again, I could take bread from the cupboard and milk from the cellar. When Mother came home in the evening she would get us something hot to eat.

When she had gone, doors were opened in other parts of the house, and from the yard and the street could be heard the heavy steps of men going off to work. The women and children were not astir yet. I crawled back to bed and fell asleep again.

When I opened my eyes again, my younger brothers were standing beside me in their shirts and the little one was crying for Mother. Getting up quickly, I fed them, put on their trousers, and took them outside. The youngest one was still crying, and my wakened sense of responsibility tried to think of something nice for him to do. As there were no other children about yet, I took them both to the nearby common, on the edge of which were some thinned-out old birch trees, and began to explain to them how the birds were singing and the flowers growing in the earth. Then the young one calmed down a little.

The day seemed very long. When children appeared in the yard, we joined them, and my younger brothers gradually forgot the unhappy morning. But my anxiety merely increased. My own pals went off someplace and I could not go with them. I had to stay in the yard with all the small children, and when I could play with them no longer I merely watched them at their games. The minutes crawled past so slowly that it felt as if the world were standing still.

When the others were called in to eat, I took my brothers inside, gave them bread and butter and milk, and I too ate my fill. This put new life into me, and when, outside again, I saw my gang going off for a swim, I decided to take my brothers with me. My sturdy middle brother set off briskly beside the bigger boys, but the youngest could not keep up. At first I forgot to take his hand and attached myself to the others, but he began to lag behind and call out in distress. I had to rush back and console him and suit my pace to his. The others were soon lost to sight and we didn't see them again until we got to the beach.

This was the one bright spot in the day. I had a swim and undressed my brothers so that they too could splash about in the warm water. But on the way home dejection again overcame me. My small brother got so tired that I had to carry him the rest of the way home and put him to bed for a while. We had used up all the milk in the morning and had to make do with bread and butter.

When the men came home from work, the yard began to empty. All the families were sitting down to their dinners and there was the feel of evening in the air. But there was no sign of Mother for a long, long while.

By the time she did come home, we were tired out. But she herself seemed excited, for in her pocket she had a nice piece of coffee cake which she had been given and in her mind the knowledge that after she had finished work the next day she would be given the money she had earned, the first money she had earned since she was married. In addition, her work had been praised by the master and mistress of the house.

But it was now too late for Mother to start getting a hot meal ready as he had promised in the morning. Our next-door neighbor had taken in the milk which the farmer had brought us in the morning and Mother went to fetch it. We again had bread and butter and milk, and as soon as we had eaten we all went to bed and were soon fast asleep.

Such was our life as it now became. Now and then Mother would be at home for a few days, feed us well, clean the room, wash and mend our clothes, go herself, or send me with coffee to Father. Then she would move on to some other place as a washerwoman and we had to fend for ourselves as best we could. Gradually we got used to our new life. The youngest stopped crying for Mother and began to turn more and more to me, and I made the best of my lot.

I began to understand what it was I had been seeking so urgently for so long. I must have been seeking new sides of myself which were now slowly coming to life.

VI

When summer had changed to autumn I had to go back to school. But I was not the same boy who had left it in the spring.

Our class was moved from the smaller building to the larger one, and instead of a woman teacher we had a man, whom later, in the higher grades, I came to like very much. Books and homework increased, and our class lessons changed more and more from games to serious effort. The running races during recess, in which I had been such a leading light, were left to the new boys in the lower class; our class began to practice the rudimentary holds on the gymnastic apparatus in the playground, to play football, to run races. I may have had a bent for one of these things too, but my love of sport was dead for a long time to come. I tried to join the small group of those who had no need of moving about even at recess. They usually gathered in a little cluster and talked about their lessons. Even among them I did not feel at home; I was merely an outside listener. But when school began, I did try to escape from my loneliness.

Even this attempt came to naught. Something happened which left a deep wound in my heart.

On one or two occasions Mother had complained to the mistress of the house where she did the washing that she did not earn enough to get new clothes for the children as they outgrew or wore out their old ones; so one of these ladies who belonged to a women's institute provided her with trousers and a shirt to fit me. I had then been back at school for two or three weeks. I recognized the clothes at once as the same which the boys from the orphanage wore—there were two of them in my class—but I put them on, happy and unsuspecting. It was, however, a great and distressing mistake. Everyone thought it natural that the orphanage boys had to wear whatever was given to them, but it branded me, who had a home, as a beggar.

A beggar!

When I came to school in the morning with these clothes on, no one said anything at first; but I saw astonishment and scorn in many eyes. And at recess a group of the more daring boys clustered round me. They asked where I had got my new clothes or whether I had been put in the orphanage. I felt the blood rush to my head. Wherever I looked I saw the glitter of derisive laughter in the boys' eyes. And when I said nothing, they spoke. They knew why such clothes were given. They touched my shirt and trousers. They wanted to know which lady my mother had been begging from.

Begging, begging! No one knew a more contemptible existence than that of a beggar. A beggar, a beggar!

In my fury I flung the nearest boy to the ground, I seized another by the throat. I lashed out with my fists and kicked with my boots. My strength boiled up so violently that the whole line of besiegers began to waver and retreat farther away from me. Perhaps the expression on my face silenced them and crushed their will to fight. Although I managed to hit several boys, no one hit me.

The two orphanage boys were standing further away looking at me quite vacantly, but watching to see what would happen. The boys whom I had tried to talk to had turned their backs to me. There was not one to whom I could turn. Although I had got the better of the scoffers with my fists, I was suddenly an outcast, degraded below them all.

I was now made to know more plainly than ever before what loneliness meant.

A beggar's son. Your mother is a beggar, and you're wearing clothes your mother begged.

As the knot of jeerers gave way somewhat, the thought came to me that I must run away from school at once, and at the same time from home. Home had disgraced me. But I had only taken a few steps when the bell suddenly rang and I stopped. As the others began moving towards the door, the sound of the bell reminded me of the unexplainable power of school, to whose authority I had long submitted. Instinctively I was aware that whoever had once been bound to it mentally would never be free. Not even if he fled to the ends of the earth. A person is bound to it by his heart, and he must bear it either as a pleasant and light load or as a burdensome and heavy one according to how faithfully he does his task.

Not even a beggar's son could run away.

I had to go to my place in the line and march with the others into the classroom, listen to what the teacher said, answer his questions, and learn as much about everything as I could.

When we came out in the next break, I kept to myself, nor did anyone come near me. All that day and for many days to come I was quite alone.

Things seemed different when I got home, too. Mother was away again washing somewhere, and as I entered the room I found my youngest brother in tears. His trousers were down and his legs and part of the floor were dirty. There was no sign of our middle brother, and the youngest one had had no one to help him. I had to take off his trousers and wash his legs and the dirty part of the floor. As I could not find his other trousers, I had to stay in and keep him company until Mother at last came home. By then it was so late that as soon as we had had something to eat we were all glad to go to bed.

The shadow which I had long felt to be there was deepening.

At school they gradually forgot who I was and what kind of clothes I wore, but I did not forget. After some weeks I dared now and again to approach the circle of chattering boys and listen silently to their talk, but inside I was alone even then.

Chapter Four

I

I was doing my homework by the light of our small lamp when Father opened the door and came in quietly. Having taken off his coat and hat, he hung them on the rack beside the door where his and Mother's best clothes hung, covered with a sheet, and sat down in his rocking chair. For a long time we were both silent, then Father said with a wan smile, "Do you recognize me?"

"Yes," I answered, startled at the strangeness of his voice.

But I can remember nothing else about his homecoming. It wasn't until a day or two later that I noticed he dragged his right leg when he walked and his right hand shook when he lifted food to his mouth. Otherwise he seemed the same as ever, spending his free time quietly in the rocking chair with his youngest son dreaming in his arms.

After a while he went to work, but he did not get back into

his former independent contract gang. It was probably one of the most humiliating consequences of his illness, though he alone was not to blame. As a building material, cement was beginning to compete with stones, and the stoneworkers' contracts were diminishing alarmingly. Several of the older men in the gang were already at an age when they could no longer compete with the younger ones, and a man who had fallen ill with tuberculosis before Father—but who was looked on as boss because he could write and had a good head for figures—grew unfit for work altogether. For reasons such as this, the younger men wound up the whole enterprise and founded a new one, which the older and sick men were not allowed to join.

But about this same time, when Father had his private troubles and the reputation of stoneworkers began to grow dim, the position of the much despised municipal works rose. Water mains were to be installed in the town and the harbor was to be enlarged. On the highest part of the rock near us they began to put up a water tower, and trenches for the pipes were dug in the streets. This was the work that my father now had to do. Spades and crowbars were not enough for digging the trenches; in the rocky parts, the way had to be cleared by blasting. Boring holes in the rock for the dynamite was also a stonemason's work; but the men who had split and dressed foundation stones and the ornamental stonework of the wealthier houses rather looked down on it. Nor could the fixed wages paid by the town hold a candle to the rates freely agreed on for contract work.

I often ran across Father now at this kind of job. Since he was earning money again, Mother gave up most of her outside washing, keeping only two or three of the best places, and began to look after her children once more. To make a little extra income, she took on the daily cleaning out of the drain common to our whole yard. The new sauna stoker had not wanted to tackle such a dirty job. In this way Mother had time to look after Father as well as the children and take coffee along to him every day. Once I went with her and I noticed that at work Father seemed brighter than at home and, encouraged by this, I often went to see him on my way home from school.

Indeed, among his fellow workers Father always showed his best side. Although drillers did not have the same status as skilled stonemasons, they were nevertheless a cut above common laborers. And Father seemed to feel this. Drilling into the rock was only for those who could make even stone open up to receive the water mains. Digging tools were no use at all.

To make things even more interesting for me, one of Father's workmates was a deaf mute. I seemed to notice that some of the men made fun of him when he didn't understand what they said. But Father thought a great deal of him as he was young and brisk and good at his job. They took the drilling in turns; one of them would sit feeding the drill while the other made it bite into the rock by striking it with a sledge hammer. For the best results, the first man had to turn his drill with straight, regular movements, and the second man had to aim his blows without wavering. The two men seemed to get on very well, even though one of them could neither hear nor speak and the other dragged his leg and held the tools with a trembling hand.

When I came up to them I would sit down on a boulder and, clutching my schoolbooks, watch them at work. Father looked over at me and the deaf mute would smile at me and make gestures, trying to explain something which I could not quite understand. We never spoke, but Father seemed to like my going to see him, and I myself felt that something strengthening always flowed into me. I heard the rock complain as the drill bit into its heart and I saw the gray dust rising into the air. I sensed, though unable to put my feelings into words, that a grim battle was being fought out here for our whole family, and that time after time it was won. Every morning the fight started anew and was waged wearily all day until it ended in success.

In the evenings when Father came home I could see plainly that he was exhausted. First he always sat at the table over a cup of coffee, and his right hand shook so badly that he spilled coffee down his chin and chest. When he had finished, he put a plug of tobacco in his mouth, moved into his rocking chair, and took the youngest child in his arms. He had always sat there in silence, but now he often closed his eyes, and such heavy tiredness settled on his face that he seemed oblivious of everything but his own distress. It was never mentioned, but I saw that Mother too would stop now and then to look at him thoughtfully, sensing the more somber future that lay ahead.

When Father got up from the table, I could sit down in his place and open my schoolbooks. They were the only books I knew that winter. Our small lamp burned on the table, and its light reached only around me. The lamp hanging from the ceiling was lighted only occasionally on Sundays. Having started to read, I not only did my homework but read the books from cover to cover and forgot everything else— Mother, my brothers, and even Father and his illness.

There was an hour or two before supper was ready, and then I had to clear my books off the table. Everyone pressed round, and from Mother's two stoneware dishes came the same smell almost every evening—boiled potatoes and gravy with little bits of pork in it. Mother put saucers in front of the two younger children, peeled some of the hot potatoes, and ladled gravy and bits of meat on top of them. Father cut a large slice of bread for each one and spread it thinly with butter. Then we began to eat, silently and hungrily, the smaller ones from their saucers and the rest of us right from the stone dishes, using first knives to peel the potatoes and then the ladle to cover them with gravy. We finished by grasping our spoons and scooping what was left straight into our mouths.

At this time we had two or three cracked plates and a few rusty looking forks, but they were never used. Very likely we youngsters had broken the plates and spoiled the forks, and, when poverty started to threaten, they were not replaced.

When we had eaten, the smallest ones were put straight to bed and, their stomachs being full, they usually fell asleep at once. Father lighted the lantern and went to the cellar to chop wood for the next day. He no longer emptied the slop pail or fetched clean water as before; because of his illness, I suppose, these tasks now fell to Mother. I sat down beside the lamp for a little longer to go on reading and let my imagination wander off on exciting journeys. When Mother and Father had done their chores, evening was considered to have changed to night, and the lamp was put out. Soon the room was filled with the sound of the family asleep, the children's breathing light and that of the adults heavy with sighs.

By degrees we got used to our present way of life and our reduced circumstances. For the younger children it was easy; they could remember nothing of the past and had no forebodings about the future. Father seemed to learn to resign himself to his present fate more quickly than Mother. She still seemed to be anxious and groping for help; but it was more apparent in the way she now and again tried to find a cure for Father's illness. She would talk to people who had suffered from the same disease and she kept urging Father to try the same treatment that had helped them to regain their health. But he showed no interest in what she told him, partly because he only trusted the doctor who had been looking after him and partly because nowadays he was apathetic to life in general. The body brought pain and it had to work in order to

113

get food, but his spiritual self lost its love of life more and more as he resigned himself to his fate.

II

The whole winter I kept to myself. All the neighbors' boys of my own age drifted away from me and our friendship was broken off. But when the cold began to lose its grip and the darkness gave way to light, my schoolbooks alone were no longer enough to interest me. Now and then I had to go to the steps to see what the others were doing. I didn't join them, but watched them from the side, although at this time I felt the cold very much and after standing still for a little while I began to shiver.

Later in the spring, when school broke up, my restlessness became more intense, but I still could not associate with the other boys. Having gone my own secret ways the whole winter, I could not find the path back to the other boys.

One Sunday I asked Father for a few coppers so that I could treat myself to a sticky bun or something else nice. But Father had no money at all. He looked at me for a moment thoughtfully, then got up from his rocking chair and went over to the chest of drawers in which he kept the little belongings that he valued. After rummaging about he found a piece of fishing line complete with float and hook.

"What about going fishing?" he asked. "I'll lend you my sheath knife and you can make a rod. You'll probably find worms in the bog over there."

I was eager to go at once. I took the line and the knife, got a rusty old tin can from the cellar, and set off for the nearby bog, where there were not only worms but also long, straight, saplings of birch and willow which made excellent rods. I picked out a young birch, cut off all the branches and the top, which was too thin, and peeled off the bark until the stem

114

was smooth and clean. Onto this I fastened the line that Father had given me and then went to the dampest part of the dried-up bog to look for worms. When I had a dozen or two in my tin, I ran off down to the water's edge.

The fishermen on this side of our island usually fished at the tip of the point, the same one where I had once gone swimming with Father when I was tiny. I rushed straight there with my rod and went right to the small rock from which the old fishermen said they got the best catch. There were two of them now when I arrived, sitting huddled silently on the rocks by the water's edge. The day was warm and sunny. A few people could be seen splashing about in the water along the point. A warm, gentle breeze was wafting from the south, where the widest part of the Gulf of Finland could be seen between the islands and the far-off line where sea and sky met. The water was glistening in the bright sunlight and near at hand it formed little ripples. I stuck a worm onto the hook, climbed on the nearest rock, and threw my line into the water.

I could not sit still like the old men. When I glanced at them, it seemed as if they didn't bother very much about their floats bobbing in the water. They either dozed or gazed at the horizon, the outline of the islands, or the sky, and let their rods rest. But I kept my eyes glued to my float. I had to stand up, to be ready every second to snatch my fish as soon as it took the bait. Excitement had seized me when Father gave me his knife and old fishing line and now it grew more and more intense.

But on this day I learned at last the art of fishing. My excitement lasted perhaps a couple of hours and the whole time I kept changing my rod from one spot to the next; all I caught was a couple of very small perch and a bleak. Then all at once I felt tired and sat down as quiet as the old men on top of a rock. I was no longer on the rock where they were still crouching, but some distance away and at exactly the same spot where I had once dipped my body in the sea for the first time. By now I was not thinking of anything; my mind was a blank, and my brain seemed to have stopped functioning and to be dozing. Nevertheless I was aware of what was going on, though not in the same way as before. I knew that I was by the sea, under a bright, warm sky, with the quiet lapping of the water and the murmur of the breeze in my ears. And at the same time I felt that I had stopped being *me*. I was only a tiny speck of the universe, like the rock on which I was sitting, like the tree that was growing not far away, like the minnows swimming about in shoals near my feet. We splinters might constantly change and move about, grow and disappear, but it could make no difference to the whole.

This mood of mine seemed to raise me up, lift me away from myself and my small needs, and make me part of eternity; all my small actions, even my fishing, were the same futile game as the ripple of the water on the shore. And I was filled with a peace that nothing could threaten.

I have no idea how long I sat there—perhaps an hour, perhaps two. The sun's position in the sky moved slowly, the shapes of the clouds kept changing behind the nearby boulders, trees, and bushes, and behind me too a shadow appeared —the old familiar shadow. But that day I was not afraid of it, in fact I liked it.

Not until a faint chill came wafting on the breeze did my float suddenly bob down out of sight. I had been gazing into the distance, but I saw the movement at once and began to haul my catch up. My prisoner struggled hard, and I had to pull with all my strength before I saw an unusually large perch rise from the depths. I was so startled that I didn't dare to take hold of the fish as the old men did, but flung it onto the ground between the rocks. There it was easy to remove the hook and to thread the perch onto the same forked twig where I had already put the smaller fish.

For a perch caught with an ordinary hook and line, this one was unusually big, weighing about a pound. Even after I had stuck it on the twig it fought desperately, flapping and twisting its tormented body. I felt no pity for it, only the pride of a victor. I hurried back to my rock, put another worm on the hook, and threw the bait into the water.

My general mood continued; it had merely taken on more colors and forms. It was broadened and enriched. It had combined my peace and my excitement in a way that is hard to explain. I could sit down again on top of my rock, lower the rod into my lap, and let my gaze wander untroubled on the far-off limits of the world. But at the same time my fishing meant something else besides making me a mere quivering speck in the universe. Things had to be looked at simultaneously from two points of view—that of the universe and that of the individual. To the universe, my victory over the big perch meant nothing at all, but to the perch it meant a painful death and to me an enormous achievement.

This thought, this vision, this mood of mine, became my deliverer during the early part of the summer. It lifted me up day by day, it gave color and form to my days and nights, to my waking moments and to my sleep.

But I caught no more fish that day. As evening drew on, other fishermen came down to the water—a couple of middle-aged men, a youth, and a boy a little bigger than me. When they started throwing their lines into the water, the men who had been huddling there for so long put their things together and went away. I was feeling hungry, so I went too. When I got home my big perch was the cause of delight. Mother lifted it up joyfully for all to see and exclaimed, "This will make lovely fish soup for tomorrow. Where did you get it?"

The smaller ones crowded round her to admire the monster, and even Father got up from his rocking chair to look at it more closely. "Why, the lad's got quite a catch," he murmured.

Early next morning, the minute I'd had my coffee and sandwiches, I set off fishing, first to the bog to look for worms, then down to the water. As on the day before, two old men were there, but only one of them was the same. The other I could not recall ever having seen. I sat down again on the rock from which I had caught the big perch, threw my bait into the water, lowered the rod into my lap, and gave myself up to the slow passing of time.

Outwardly, this day was more varied than the day before, but inwardly it was the same, merely perhaps the clarifying and widening of my moods. I caught no big fish, but the smaller ones were a little bigger than those of the day before and there were more of them. Now and then I changed my place, continuing to sit as silent as the old men and, like them, gazing at the distant shapes of the earth and sky. From time to time they changed, some going away and others coming in their stead. I lived in a kind of timelessness, in which the coming and going of the fishermen meant no more than the changing patterns of the waves and clouds. When evening came again and I went home to bed with my catch, that too was merely something the same as the setting of the sun for the night behind the treetops on the islands to the left.

I had suddenly stepped into the middle of a completely new summer. I had become a different person from what I had been before. Every morning I wandered down to the water with the rod on my shoulder, even when it was raining or clouds covered the sun. At home I spoke in the same way as before; when the weather grew still warmer and boys from our yard came down to swim, I would sometimes join them in the water. Nevertheless, I was not the same as I had been.

Mother and Father would often glance at each other, and the boys shouting noisily on the beach would suddenly fall silent in embarrassment when I said what I thought was some ordinary word. What did I say? I cannot explain, but even then I sensed proudly that I touched certain spots in them, the existence of which people like to ignore because they cannot understand them. That summer I began to be called "the rum fisherman," by the boys in particular, but sometimes by the grownups as well. But it didn't upset me, because as a rule I was alone, and the few times I did spend with others I was like a stranger.

As Father's income was still very small, Mother went off several times this summer to load ships at the docks. If possible, she liked to get on to the small sailing ships that put in for shingles, as the work on these was particularly well suited to women and children; it was lighter and called for greater speed than the loading of timber. The wages were less than for the heavier work, but better than those earned by washerwomen.

It was on those shingle boats a few years later that I too began trying to earn my living. Now they were only a nuisance to me, as my younger brothers were left in my care all day. I took them with me down to the beach and got them used to the sea. The mornings always went well. While I sat on a rock fishing, they would play in the sand, paddle at the edge of the water, throw stones as far as they could, and stand still every now and then to gaze at the vastness of the world. But as midday approached, the youngest one especially grew tired and fretful, both of them were hungry, and we had to go home. And when I had fed them sandwiches and milk I had to stay at home while the youngest took a nap. Then I took them down to the beach again, but the afternoons were never very quiet. My middle brother was still quite happy to spend his time by the water, but the youngest one for some reason was often fidgety. He didn't want to play any more, but kept crying and wanting Mother. So I could not always stay up in the heights of eternity, but had to come down to earth to console him.

Usually it took two or three weeks to load a boat. When it was full of shingles and sailed away, Mother would stay home for a while to wash our clothes, clean the house, air the bedclothes thoroughly, bake a large pile of bread, brew a large barrel of ale, and do lots of other odd jobs. At these times I was free once more to be alone by the sea and live in my dream world.

The early part of the summer glided warmly past. For a long time I was unaware of the passing of the days, weeks, and months, for there were no changes in eternity, only tiny ripples. I even drifted away from my parents. It was good to be alone.

III

This same summer I came to know the countryside too for the first time. Because of Father's illness and our poverty I had a chance to go for five weeks at the end of the summer to a summer colony for the children of poor parents. As I was sent there twice after that and the events and moods of the different visits are all mixed up in my mind, I cannot describe them in any proper sequence. The main thing, I think, is for me to try to tell what I experienced in general during these visits, especially since a new kind of shadow obscured the following winters. From the fishermen I had learned how to open up my first path away from reality and by degrees I came to know many other paths of the same kind. As my early years became more and more gloomy, life without them would have been impossible.

Even then I kept repeating the words of my last Christmas

about goodness and beauty. And with these words in my mind, I set off on these journeys. They did not always help me to be good, but they did encourage me to be what I was.

In what way did Mother, who saw me off at the station, look at me as the carriages glided past her and she knew that she was parting from her eldest son for five weeks? For the whole of the train journey I saw her face in my thoughts, which wandered about as in a sad dream. She sensed, and I knew, that during these weeks in particular much would develop within me which would cause us to drift apart still farther.

I did not begin to come to life until the train arrived at the little country station. The other children and I got into a large, rumbling cart. We left the railway and the clusters of houses behind us and drove on and on along a winding, dusty road. The pine woods soughing on the heather-clad heaths and the thick clumps of firs sighing in the breeze no longer spoke to us of the sea. Even the air was different—drier and lighter than the air we were used to. In addition, we no longer saw the line where the sky arching above us met the sea, as on the shore of our island. Everything vanished, everything hid itself in the mysterious forests. Now and then we caught sight of small farms and fields, tiny clearings in the middle of the forest. But in spite of everything we shouted for joy, laughed, chattered, and yelled. We were no longer the same boys and girls as before. Feelings had awakened within us which we ourselves had not known existed.

Gallop, horses, gallop! That was our dearest wish at first. We wanted to race on towards distant, unknown lands. Gallop, horses, gallop!

But the horses didn't gallop. On level ground and uphill, they plodded along, and even going downhill they jogged as lazily as ever they could. The man sitting in front of the rear wheels didn't seem to hear our shouts either, and had he not twitched at the reins now and then we should have wondered whether he was still alive. His broad back was like a human figure carved out of a huge tree. But the young man sitting by the front wheels, who we later heard was the parson's eldest son, laughed and grinned at us the whole time, saying we were just like calves let out into the meadow in the spring after being shut up in the barn all winter.

And perhaps he was right. We were overjoyed to feel that we were approaching freedom.

There was very little of it, however, the first day. When we drew up in the big open space in front of a fairly small, old manor house, our first thought was to run off in all directions in search of the secrets hidden even in the immediate vicinity; but the teachers in charge of us nipped this little excursion in the bud by calling us sharply back and collecting us round them. We had to take our things inside to the places allotted us beside our beds; then we were marched down in twos to the river to wash and swim, then marched back to the meal tables.

Even so we saw a lot of new and exciting things. We saw our beds, made up with dazzling white sheets and soft, warm, gray blankets, standing side by side, the boys' beds in one room and the girls' in another. We knew at once that when we got into bed our teachers would leave us in peace and we should be free to lie there smelling the fresh straw in the mattress and whispering to each other to our hearts' content.

Down by the shore we saw the river. Some of us had seen it at its mouth, with the waterfall and the log jams. But here we saw the river gliding along between the trees, free, dark, out of reach of the winds, its gently flowing surface like hard luster. Here too logs drifted past now and then, but their course was carefully marked out, and there were long intervals when nothing could be seen but the booms that guided them. The shadows of the forest rested in the water as though

122

drawn for eternity. The reeds near the bank trailed dreamily in their most brilliant green, and white and yellow water lilies, which down near the sea were only to be found in one or two sheltered inlets undisturbed by people, spread out like eyots at the edge of the reeds. In midstream two birds were swimming in solemn splendor, utterly indifferent to our shouting.

This very first time we went swimming, some of us would suddenly stop in the middle of our boisterous games as if to listen to something. Those of us who had grown up with the perpetual murmur of the sea heard amidst the shouts of our playmates something strange, almost frightening—the mysterious silence of the forest.

By suppertime we were beginning to feel tired. The food was good, and we ate hungrily, as boys always do when they have used up a lot of energy. Our excited and eager conversations flagged, even without the teachers' admonitions. We gradually fell silent, and when we saw the shadows lengthening on one side of the house and beside the trees and felt a chill in the evening air our thoughts stood still. Where were we now? Where was Mother? Where was Father? Who were all these strangers?

Or perhaps it was only we smaller ones, the newcomers, who so quickly forgot the great and exciting events we had just experienced.

Night drew on.

As we had not yet been divided into groups, some of the bigger boys and girls were told to help the cook with the washing up. The rest of us were sent straight to bed.

"They're tired from the journey," the teachers said to each other, smiling contentedly.

On this evening we didn't whisper anything to each other as we had imagined we would. From under the bedclothes here and there came the stifled sound of sobbing, but no one said a word. We were thinking of our homes and our parents, and we soon fell asleep.

But next day, and on all the days that followed, we had forgotten the twinges of misery and alarm of that first evening. First thing in the morning we were given large mugs of milk and big sandwiches—bigger mugs and tastier sandwiches than we ever got at home. We were divided into groups—some to be cook's helpers, some to weed the kitchen garden, others to help the washerwoman, a fourth group to sweep the yard. We went for a swim three times, we played football, we played hide-and-seek with the girls. Some were even allowed to go rowing on the river. During the morning we had the first real meal of the day; in the afternoon we had dinner, and in the evening we were given a large helping of porridge and milk. There was coming and going all day long —we ran about all over the place—and lots of new things had to be learned. By the time evening came we no longer felt strange; everything was already familiar. Our beds were not strange beds any more. We felt at home. Mother and Father were almost forgotten.

Some may have been sobbing under the bedclothes on this second evening, but, if so, they were so quiet that no one heard them. The teachers said proudly that they had a nice cheerful lot of children and none of them need be sent home.

During the days that followed, I grew and filled out quickly. I found I was a good swimmer and a good football player, and I held my own in the scuffles with the bigger boys of the colony and the still bigger boys at the parsonage. At such moments I could once more throw myself into the game with the same exuberant spirits as at school, before Father's illness. I forgot myself, remembering nothing about either good or evil. I doubted nothing, I feared nothing, and success was with me at every step.

The dark side of myself I never wanted to see again. I

should have been quite happy to do nothing but eat, play football, swim, and sleep.

But one had to do other things as well. One had to join the others in the group in tasks of various kinds and win the special favor of the cook, the washerwoman, and the teachers. And these tasks brought me face to face with new and strange aspects of my personality. I couldn't help washing the dishes so clean that the cook did not have to put a single one back in the sink; often she took them to show as a sample of what well-washed dishes should look like. When helping the washerwoman, I found it impossible to slink away; I had to stay near her and do whatever she told me. When weeding the kitchen garden, I was forced to pull out every single weed and help the useful plants to grow and give them all the water they needed. When sweeping the yard, I couldn't leave the tiniest piece of rubbish lying about. To the joy of the teachers, I even had to brush everything up that was in my area. I knew quite well beforehand how scornfully the boys, and most of the girls too, watched me, but still I was forced to do these queer things. Funny little things.

Though I forgot home and my father, I could not for one moment forget my loneliness.

I knew that a child's world was constantly at war with the ridiculous world of grownups. Though children nearly always had to obey grownups and though they often loved them, they rebelled against them in their own way in order to make the stupidity of grownups tolerable, at least up to a point. But my spiritual self had long ago been removed from this company of the blessed and had become a solitary pilgrim on life's road.

There were one or two others like me at the colony, but I was glad they didn't belong to my group and I avoided them. Sometimes I hated them almost as if they were the worst side of myself.

Sometimes I tried to rebel against my benefactors, but even this could not put me back into the boys' world that I longed for. The second time I was at the colony, the following happened. Some of the boys had been up to mischief and for this reason a common punishment was given to all the boys— none of us was allowed to go swimming. As a rule we were the first to run down to the river, while the girls remained beside the sandy path leading down to the bank to await their turn. But on the day of the punishment our great and honorable privilege was revoked. It was our turn to have to dawdle about by the path and to watch the girls run off giggling and to listen to their shouts of glee and the splashing of water from behind the trees on the river bank. Watch and listen to this feminine triumph. One of the teachers sat with us as a guard. We didn't speak, but stared at the ground and let the hot sun shine down on our necks while our anger smoldered. "One day, one day," the most daring of us thought, "we'll have grown so strong that this can be avenged."

When the girls returned from their swim, giggling just as much as before they went, we thought for a moment that we had paid for our mischief and would be allowed down to the river even in our disgraced state. But again we were frustrated. When the girls had gone by, we were ordered back to the house. We were not allowed even close enough to the river to get the smell of the water.

The teacher stood up and began walking slowly towards the house, and the boys followed him as slowly and angrily as they dared. But boyish fear had suddenly left me completely. I stood up as slowly as they did and as slowly as they followed the teacher I began to walk towards the river. All alone. I could feel in my back how the boys were staring at me, but I didn't turn my head. Excitedly I waited for something special to happen, perhaps now I would have to bear the burden of some even bigger punishment all by myself. But for some reason nothing happened. The teacher didn't notice that I had gone, and not even the astonished whispering of the other boys drew his attention to me. We lost sight of each other. I went down to the river bank, and the others went up to the house.

Not even now was my absence observed.

When I got down to the river, I undressed and swam for a long time in full view of the washerwoman. She was horrified. She waved her arms and shouted, "Come out at once! I'll tell the teachers if you don't come out at once and go with the others. You disobedient little boy!"

But I went on swimming for as long as I liked. Then I came out of the water, got dressed, and walked up after the others. The boys gaped at me, still expecting something awful to happen. But nothing did. The girls and the teachers had not even noticed that I had been away.

Even then I used to think sometimes that there was a vacuum where I was concerned and that my existence was nothing but a figment of the imagination.

Even this prank of mine did not bring me back to the boys' world; in fact, because of such acts, I found myself more and more alone. The boys were almost awestruck that I was never punished. And it worried me too. Naturally the boys never gave me away. But why did the washerwoman not report my escapade? For several agonizing days I waited for her to speak of it. But she never told the teachers about it, and to her friend the cook she only whispered it weeks later. They both looked at me and chortled to themselves.

Once I lied to the matron's face about another happening, and not even then did she doubt I was speaking the truth. This was the third time I was at the colony and by then I was a big boy.

When our group was down by the river helping the washerwoman we were allowed to go swimming as much as we liked. Once I had a bet with a pal of mine that I could swim as far as the log boom near the opposite bank and back again with my clothes on. I don't remember whether I thought I'd win a few coppers or what the stake was. At any rate I put on my moleskin trousers and my small linen coat—they were the only clothes I had and I wore them the whole summer—and jumped into the water. From the very first strokes I found that I was making very little headway and that it would take much longer than usual to cover the distance. My trousers had suddenly become a heavy load tied to my bottom and dragging them through the water required an enormous effort. But I never doubted for a moment that victory was not already within my grasp. The yells of the other boys urged me on and accompanied me as I swam happily across. For some reason the washerwoman was not down by the water just then.

As I neared the boom, the boys' shouts died away, their voices sounded faint and indistinct, but I swam quietly on. Having reached the boom, I turned around and started to swim back. After every stroke I expected to hear their shouts again, louder and clearer, but I was disappointed. The boys were all standing at the end of the jetty watching me in silence. Instead of their shouts I suddenly heard the clanging of the dinner bell. A couple of them went at once to the bank and slipped up towards the house, but the others lingered, seized by doubt and indecision. The dinner bell was calling them, and the strict orders connected with it started them moving slowly, but it was not easy to leave me alone. They had made a bet with me and that alone obliged them to wait and see who would win.

Suddenly two of them pushed the boat into the water and rowed quickly towards me.

"Get into the boat," one of them said, "or we'll be late for dinner."

"Then I'd lose the bet," I replied. "I'm going to swim all the way to the bank."

I swam out of their reach so that they would not haul me up by the scruff of the neck, and after trying to persuade me for a while they rowed back to the shore as quickly as they had come. The dinner bell had stopped ringing, and it was easy to guess that all the others were now sitting down to dinner. The boys on the bank went on waving to me for a few moments and talking excitedly. Then they too ran off and disappeared.

I felt a heavy, empty silence spread suddenly all around me. I was swimming all alone in the river. I saw the forest and the clouds in the sky, but not a single human being. For a few seconds some indescribable terror tried to seize me and snatch me away from the world of men. I swam for dear life and with every ounce of strength I had. But just as unaccountably as I had been on the verge of yielding to panic, I suddenly felt quite calm again. I slowed down my strokes to normal and swam the rest of the way in almost an exalted frame of mind. I felt I was doing something that not everyone was capable of.

Having reached the bank, I hurried up towards the house. I thought at first of running to our dormitory and changing my jacket for a dry shirt, but instead I turned in under the old birch trees where the big meal table stood. Changing my clothes would have taken too long. I was going to try to slink into my seat without anyone noticing, but the eldest teacher saw me and called me to her.

"Where have you been? Just now there were four late-comers and you're the fifth."

For a second I wondered what I would say, then I had a flash of inspiration.

"Please, teacher, my jacket was so dirty that I had to wash it. I meant to go and change but I didn't have time."

The teacher stood up, examined first my front and then my

back. Her angry expression vanished, and her face shone with pride.

"Why, yes, this does look as if it had been washed. The other boys said they had been out rowing, which is forbidden, but this one prefers to keep his clothes clean. Look, everyone, how well he has washed it."

"It looks clean enough," the cook said in surprise, and the other teachers agreed that there was nothing wrong with my jacket.

No one seemed to have noticed that my trousers too were sopping wet. I went to my seat and began eating greedily, not daring to look about me. I didn't even give a quick glance to see what the boys were thinking. They must have been wondering again how it was possible for me to transform a blatant act of disobedience into a cause for praise. Nor did I myself understand how I could fool the adults.

I was to hear of this incident years later. At some gathering at my younger brother's school, Mother met the woman who had been the matron this particular summer. When the matron heard my mother's name, she began praising me and my laundry skill, in particular. Never before or since had she seen anybody with a white jacket as clean as mine after I had washed it myself. When we got home, Mother was naturally curious to hear how I had done it as she had never seen me wash a garment in my life, but I didn't tell her what had really happened.

Happenings of this kind made me still more aware of myself. I could no longer imagine that I was lonely merely because of Father's illness and the poverty it brought with it. By degrees I was forced to realize that the basic cause was within me.

As I said, however, during our football games and when we went swimming, the boys looked up to me. This gave me some kind of satisfaction. But I only felt happy when our group had the day off and we could go rowing on the river. Here I learned how to handle a rowboat and I took this skill back with me to the city.

The river flowed into a large lake, then continued slowly past us to join a bigger river and traveled with it to the sea. If we went downstream, we came first to the splendid slopes of the parsonage and a large farm with its wide fields. Beyond the bridge the riverbanks were sheltered by silent forests, which after about a kilometer allowed the river to spread out into the lake. This was still not the big, famous lake on which the steamers plied and from which the biggest river rose, but even this silence that opened out seemed vast and made my head reel. When we stepped ashore there, our feet sank into clean, brown sand and dragged as though heavy with fatigue. From the sparse clumps of rushes, large and unfamiliar birds rose into the air. Despite the vast extent of our view we could not see a single human being or dwelling, not the tiniest field or other sign of man's work except a small, rotting rack for drying nets and an even more dilapidated boat that had been left to lie forgotten on the shore. Once the teachers brought us to this spot for a walk, and as we went along we made more boisterous and excited noise than usual. But when we got here and saw the huge expanse of the lake widening out, the insignificant little bunch of us fell silent. None of us felt inclined to go for a swim, although this sandy beach was known to be an ideal spot. We didn't run off into the forest to see if the blueberries were ripe. We stood staring at the lake, in which the river water seemed to have come to a standstill. We gazed at the sky and the jagged outline of the forest and we listened to the silence, that same silence which had startled us the day we arrived.

We listened and watched for a moment. Then, just as

131

silent, we got back into the boat and began to row faster than usual until we regained the river and felt the water flowing once more beneath our boat.

When we set off from where we lived in the other direction, making our way with an effort upstream, we also came to a small inlet where the river widened out and the water seemed to have forgotten to move on. But it was a delightful spot. Birds flew up from the reeds by the bank and yellow water lilies, just bursting into flower, spread in such profusion that they were like a carpet on the water. The forest was so sparse that the sky gleamed through the trees on all sides. Here and there fish plopped, and when we dipped our feet over the side of the boat into the water it felt much warmer than anywhere else.

But when we went on still farther, the trees grew closer together, and the water suddenly began to flow much faster. Only at midday was the whole river lit by the sun; at other times the banks lay in deep shadow, which grew narrower on one side in the morning and gradually broadened on the other in the afternoon. Usually we stopped near a quaint little bridge, where the current gurgled and splashed and twined itself into eddies. The river here formed a small waterfall.

Once the teachers brought us here along the riverside footpaths, and we felt frightened but happily excited as we crossed the bridge. It was a plank bridge slung on thick ropes and seemed to have been put there for people who wanted to cross the river, but the cows and horses put out into the forest for the summer dared not use it. We were nervous when we felt it swaying. The first time we all went across it, even the boys, their faces set, held on tightly to the guide ropes and the girls screamed. But when only a few of us stepped onto it after that, its swaying did not frighten us any more. We were silent here for different reasons altogether. The clinking of the cowbells from the forest, the eddies in the water and its busy ripple, the slowly lengthening shadows, and the drowsy murmur of the trees—all these sounds and the calm in the midst of them silenced us.

Or is this only my imagination? If one of my companions on these outings were to start recalling our times together, he might tell of very different things.

But these are my memories, for this was one of the best stops along the road of my life. I made no friends there, but always when we returned home after our five weeks' stay, I had put on a lot of extra weight.

IV

In the autumn following my first visit to the summer colony—the same summer when I learned to fish—I had to move for a year to the Hovinsaari school. The city's population was growing so fast that not even all the former pupils could be accommodated in the old school building in the center of town. It meant a longer walk for me in the mornings, about half as far again, but otherwise the transfer did me a lot of good. Hovinsaari at that time had the city's newest, finest and biggest school. Nearly all the boys were strangers to me. I didn't know them and they didn't know me, and this was a good thing.

Part of my way to school took me through the woods, and after that past the house where I used to live, before I got to the main Hovinsaari road. My first playmate, the boy who had broadened my outlook in so many ways, had been going to the Hovinsaari school the whole time and was still living in the same old gray cottage as before. When we renewed our friendship and found we had much the same way home, he began watching for me from his window in the mornings and ran out to join me the minute he saw me coming. He used to chatter away as we went along, so the walk to and from school always passed quickly. After our first tentative soundings, we both found that deep down we had very little in common and would never become close friends, but this did not affect our school walks.

At this school too I remained alone. The summer had given me new strength and developed my spiritual self and because of this I dared—this winter only and among boys I didn't know—to join in the games once more during recess, but my innermost self I did not reveal to a soul. The lonely must walk their own road.

At the beginning of the autumn things at home were better than they had been for a long time, as Mother was earning good extra money down at the docks. But this improved state of affairs did not last long. As the darkest part of the year approached—when a fourth child was born, the family's only girl—we again had to depend entirely on Father's income. But as far as I was concerned, the most important thing was that this autumn I got to know books which were quite different from my schoolbooks.

Soon after school started, our class was given permission to go to the school library every Saturday and borrow two books. Previously we had not been regarded as sufficiently good readers to be granted such a favor. From the very first this permission aroused intense curiosity in me. At home not a word had ever been said about books. In my whole environment literature was a completely strange world. For all that, I sensed that I belonged there, and the very first Saturday I was one of the first to hurry into the library.

Behind a long trestle table sat one of the men teachers, assisted by two of the senior boys. They got the books required from a high shelf and gave them to the teacher, who entered them in a large notebook and handed them to the applicant. You were not allowed to speak to anyone but the teacher and his assistants. On our side of the long table, wide sheets, both handwritten and printed, were fixed to the wall, and from these you could get the names of the books you wanted. The minute I entered the room I was seized by an inexplicable confusion. The silence, the restrainedly polite remarks, the mute secrets contained in the rows of books, suddenly seemed to entangle me in a web of things as yet unknown. For a long time all I could do was to stare about me in a state of deep respect.

At last a classmate whispered into my ear that if I didn't know what books I wanted I could choose them by the names on the sheets. The teacher in charge of this room which threw me into such a state of agitation glanced at us so sternly that my classmate drew away from me in fright, and I turned, flustered, to look at the lists. The names of the books meant nothing to me at all and I picked two out at random.

What could they have been, these first two books that I had ever borrowed? I can remember nothing whatever about them, but I have a vivid picture of what they did to me that day.

When I got home I sat down in the light by the window and opened one of the books. The second I started reading I became oblivious of everything else. Mother was out—it was one of her last days at work—and my younger brothers were getting noisy and restless from hunger. I was supposed to give them milk and slices of bread and butter, but I had no time to spare for that. Beg and cry as they would, I was hardly aware of their existence, for I had set off on a long, exciting journey into a world that was quite new to me.

Not until my parents came home from work and Mother gave me odd jobs to do did I gradually realize where I was and begin to feel the pangs of hunger in my own stomach. But when the jobs were done and we had had our coffee, had eaten our supper, and had made up the beds for the night, I pushed my way as usual into the lamplight. Mother and

Father, thinking I was doing my homework, said nothing. Not until some weeks later did they notice I was reading something else and become curious. They did not understand my explanations, however, and looked at the books with a puzzled expression and listened wide-eyed and with a kind of respect to what I said. Only when I forgot my chores did they get cross and even start to detest my books, but by this time books had become such an important factor in my life that I was ready to defend them at all costs.

Good and evil, beauty and ugliness, had taken on a new meaning. They were not part of our home or my school, but I knew now that it was the lone man who could attain them.

As the days got shorter and darker, the lamp had to be lighted as soon as I came home from school. It illuminated only its immediate vicinity and most of the room was in semi-darkness, out of which came the sounds made by the rest of the family—the crying of the newborn baby, the clatter of dishes, the scuffling of the smaller boys, the sighing of our tired mother, and the monotonous, and often melancholy, creak of Father's rocking chair. But I always had fresh books and I was allowed to sit in the lamplight.

The lonely one was galloping far away in the world of wild Indians and adventurers with goodness and beauty in his heart.

Our food began to get worse. Once a week, on Tuesdays I think it was, Father got his wages; on those evenings I had to go with Mother to meet him, and when we got the money we always called at a shop where we were old customers. We bought ten kilos of rye meal, most of which would be baked the next day into loaves and a little kept for making sauce, several measures of potatoes, a chunk of pork fat, a lump of butter, and a few other essentials. The first winter after my sister's arrival the bag of flour was still too heavy for me and Father had to carry it home, but by the following winter I took on the job of carrying it, though even then it made me pant. The big paper bag smelled of freshly ground rye, and I liked this very much.

On the evening of pay day we had better food than usual and could eat our fill. But the very next day things started to get worse again, and by the end of the week our stomachs were rumbling angrily. On Sunday they were somewhat appeased, as in honor of the sabbath we had real broth. But for the next two days, while we were waiting for Father's wages, the growling became all the fiercer.

Some of our neighbors began to notice that we were getting poorer, and when one of them brought home two sheep for Christmas from the farm where she used to live and roasted them in big chunks in the baking oven, she gave the melted fat to us. When it was cold it turned into smooth, dark gray clumps, which lasted for two or three months and served as fat with which to make the sauce for the potatoes. Whenever the lard bought with Father's wages gave out, our room was filled with a new smell which tickled our nostrils and throats in a way that dulled the pangs of our hunger. At first it didn't taste very good either, but gradually we got used to it.

It may have been the fault of the mutton fat that just at this time the stomach pains began which have continued all my life. Sometimes they were very severe. Especially at school a sudden griping in my belly would get so acute that I would sit writhing behind my desk, bent almost double, and with cold sweat on my brow. Several times I had to ask the teacher's permission to go out. My stomach then emptied at both ends, and after that the rest of the day passed better than usual.

But every evening a book was waiting for me at home, and I knew a way of shutting the gates of the everyday world and opening the gates of the world of imagination. I forgot neither good nor evil.

137

When the severe cold set in, my schoolmate and I would often take a short cut to school across the frozen bay and through the yard of the sawmill on the Hovinsaari side. While crossing the ice we could see the dazzling brightness of the sun more clearly than anywhere else. Sometimes we were buffeted by a blizzard, which enclosed us in its midst, isolating us from everyone else, and we could feel the icy wind whipping our cheeks. These things delighted us both. We felt them as a challenge to our strength, which had to grow and make us tougher and bolder. On that short journey I could sometimes forget everything but the zest for life latent in my punished body. But not even that lasted for very long.

One day when I was going to school alone—my companion was not well and had stayed at home—the cold wind began to mistreat me. It attacked me so fiercely that many times I fell down on the ice, and, try as I would to run, the journey took longer than ever before. I felt not only my cheeks and ears turning numb, but my whole head seemed to be turning to ice and my whole body beginning to freeze. When at last I reached the shelter of the sawmill and my thoughts began to move once more, I had to resign myself humbly to my smallness and insignificance. It seemed as if I, who had tried to take a little joy and pride in something other than books, had been given a new warning. Only in the secret world of books could the small and weak be strong and brave.

The following autumn I went back to the old school and into a class with the same teacher as before. The solitary one left his companion and the games during recess and returned to his lone walks and to standing in the schoolyard by himself. This teacher was a bachelor and was very kind, and I had liked him from the first. Now he began to like me too. Perhaps he found in me something that pleased him. He thought I was an exceptional pupil and a good boy in other ways and not a nuisance to his teacher. I did my lessons well,

138

and he pretended not to notice my weak subjects. Perhaps my poverty touched him. I was now starting the fifth grade. I had threadbare trousers and I walked to school in bare feet even when the first falls of sleet and snow covered the ground. Having no shoes, I had to spend recess too in the classroom and could quietly prepare for the next lesson.

But anything good also had its unpleasant side if it came my way. This winter the school began giving a free meal once a day to the poorest pupils. When the teacher announced this and asked who were the needy ones who would like to have a meal in the school canteen, nobody said a word. My stomach began to rumble, and my mouth watered copiously. There was the chance for a good plateful of soup or porridge every day. But when I glanced around me, I found that everyone was looking at me. They all knew who was most in need of the school's poor-man's food. How could I raise my hand then? I had to swallow all the saliva and with it the taste of food. I well remembered the orphanage clothes. I dared not raise my hand, but my cheeks, usually so pale, began to burn as though with fever.

The teacher glanced round the classroom and waited for some time, but when no one raised his hand he too looked at me. "This seems to be a class of rich people," he said. "But I think *you* had better go and have a good meal every day."

And so the matter was decided. At recess I was still left alone, but when school was over that day I had once more to fight one of the most bitter battles of my life and to lose it. Compared with others of my size, I had grown weak and feeble. The boy who had not had enough to eat was unable to fight with those who were better fed. However, it made the teacher's decision easier. After the fight it was all the same whether I went to the canteen or not. The new mark that was branded on me could not be kept secret from anyone. And I went.

Every day I went to the canteen and had a good square meal and I vomited up part of my spiritual self many many times.

From the outset there were a lot of pupils from the other classes in the canteen, and when it began to be known how good the soups and the porridge were, the desire to eat gradually overcame the shame of poverty even in our class. The following year quite a number of us turned up. But I was still alone, and in the canteen, too, I remained just as silent as on the playground.

The teacher would sometimes look at me as though in pity. Of course he knew nothing of my struggles at school or of my family circumstances, but he sensed and understood a great deal. When he heard that on Saturdays I was always the most eager to hurry across to the Hovinsaari school on the other side of town—our school had no library—his face beamed, and we became firm friends.

The winters were already beginning to seem like a dream in darkness which only artificial light was able to illuminate, however faintly. But when I was alone I still wanted to believe in goodness and sometimes dream of beauty too.

v

The winters were long and the summers short, but when memory taps on the doors of the past it finds little behind the white doors but a lot worth telling behind the green ones.

One day in the late summer—it was the same year when I had been at the summer colony ever since school got out—an unusual visitor called to see us. She was a stout woman of medium size and well-to-do appearance from one of the better-class families in our group of houses. Her husband was a cabinet maker and on Sundays, to my astonishment, he dressed in a fine dark-blue suit, a dark-blue brimmed hat, shiny black shoes, a stiff, gleaming white collar and a colored tie. Before they moved to our house I had never seen such clothes except in the center of town. Their eldest son was married and he had been made foreman of the factory where his father worked. The next two boys worked as their fathers' apprentices, and only the last two were still at school and free in the summer. The youngest was in the same class as I was, and the older one was in the grade above.

Their mother was feeling tired, and the doctor had said that she was not to do any more heavy work like washing, so she had come to ask if our mother could come and help her.

She sat in our rocking chair breathing heavily and as though sunk in the exhaustion of her body. When the baby of our family had become a little stronger and once the summer came, Mother had begun once more to work down at the docks and she shut her eyes to everything else; but having looked for a moment at her neighbor, who had always been so well, she began to feel sorry for her.

"As soon as I've finished loading the ship," she said, "I'll take a few days' off again. I was going to do our own washing anyway, so I can do yours at the same time."

Our guest brightened at once and she seemed to take a much more rosy view of life. They went on talking about the washing for a while and then the neighbor turned to me.

"Your boy seems to have put on weight, he looks quite perky," she said.

"He's been at the summer colony and could eat as much as he liked," Mother replied.

"I thought it was something like that."

The woman looked at me for a moment as though inspecting me, then she went on, "Listen! My husband bought us a boat in the spring and the whole summer our boys have been out almost every day on the islands gathering wood, and their father pays them a small wage. There's such a large pile of it now that we have enough firewood to last the winter, but they don't want to stop work yet. It occurred to me that they might as well take your boy along. It will mean less money for them, of course, but it will be company for them, and nice for him too."

I felt joy flood through my whole being. I could go rowing again to unknown shores, and this time I could listen to the secrets of the sea itself. I was so happy that I couldn't get a word out; but as Mother also liked the idea, the two women agreed that I should join the boys the very next morning if the weather was fine.

We boys did not yet know each other very well. When I appeared in front of their steps in the morning with a bottle of milk, a packet of sandwiches, and an axe under my arm, they peered at me first out of the window before they came out. I could tell they were annoyed at not getting as big a day's pay as before. But being well brought up, they at last did what their mother told them, and when they came out they tried to be as nice to me as they could. For my part I first thought of turning tail out of shame, but then I remembered the sea and stayed with them.

On this very first day, and I think even as we set off, we all forgot our initial feelings of resentment and embarrassment.

Their new boat was the same design as that used by the people of Savo, the lake province in the east of Finland, but a little higher at the sides, as was usual here on the coast of the gulf. It skimmed across the calm water as two of the boys, already skillful rowers, grasped two pairs of oars and the third put the boat on course with the steering paddle. Until now, the brothers had not noticed that they had the fastest rowboat in the bay; but this morning they realized it after a few strokes and were delighted. Housewives who lived on the islands and who had been to the market in town were rowing home, and old men were on their way out for a day's fishing.

As we sped past them all like the wind, we felt we belonged to a superior race of beings. And when not even the bulgy-sided fishing boats with their engines left us behind, our pride swelled still more. We kept up a furious speed, spurred on by the elder brother who was sitting in the stern.

As we rowed across the first inlet, I kept waiting for the wonder to happen. I had seen this inlet from our own shore hundreds of times, and sometimes I had even managed to row to the other side when we had been picking berries. But as we glided into a narrow sound unknown to me, I felt that my dream would soon come true. The woods growing on both sides of the water suddenly came as close to each other as the woods protecting the inland river. But they were not concerned with the silence of eternity, and on that first day in the rowboat when the sea was calm and the sun shone brightly, I was conscious of them wafting sea sounds from afar, and the air was filled with a heavy salt taste. Reefs composed of huge boulders and rocks apparently thrown about higgledy-piggledy had gleaming surfaces that had been licked smooth and washed clean. On our own shore they were already stained by human beings' smoke, and the autumn storms were not as free to rage there as they were here. Rowing was not as easy or safe either. Rocks were not only visible above the water, but they lurked like crouching beasts under the water, hidden by the bright-green water weeds which looked like thick moss. The channel marked out by the islanders twisted between them like a snake, and at the narrowest part of the sound it turned sharply and the helmsman had to stand up in order to see which way to steer.

But not until the sound widened like the gaping jaws of some monster did I feel the sea really touch me. Some power quite unknown to me brushed against my sweaty back. When I turned to look behind me, I saw that the horizon appeared much wider than from our own shore and that the calm surface of the sea was heaving gently in scarcely perceptible broad waves. Even more powerful, it seemed to me, was the air, which had come from away beyond the sea and which today was stirring faintly, caressing my back and licking the sweat on my forehead as I turned my head. These are things which one is only aware of through experience.

As our boat began to dip on the gleaming smooth surface of the sea, the helmsman stood up for a moment and his voice was suddenly shriller than usual.

"Straight out to sea!" he yelled. "A bit further and we can turn to the right, towards the west."

A few large solitary boulders which were resting in the water far from land had to be negotiated, as their smaller companions were lurking invisible under the water.

Those solitary boulders seemed huge to me. They were sentinels of the land. Day and night, year in year out, they stared straight at the horizon, from whose depths had come the mysterious power which had just touched me.

"Turn right, to the west!" yelled the helmsman, suddenly steering our boat in a new direction. We had just passed the outermost cluster of rocks, and for what seemed a long time the boat remained on its side as the broad, smooth wave beneath us glided slowly and was gone.

After we had rowed on for another ten minutes or so, the straggling heaps of rocks covering the outer shore of the island stopped suddenly, and a small sandy bay opened up before us. The helmsman was already sitting calmly on the after-thwart, and he steered our boat towards the shore without any words of command.

Even after we had scrambled ashore, I should have liked to gaze out to sea and listen to what it was trying to tell me, but there was no time. These brothers were hard workers and bent on business. The boat was dragged up onto the beach, and with axes under our arms we made straight for the forest.

A lot of trees had been felled here the previous winter, and pine and spruce branches were strewn all over the place. I don't know whether we were allowed to gather them up, but neither that summer nor the following one did the landowner come to disturb our work.

Before my appearance on the scene, the nearest woods had been stripped so completely that we had to push deeper in, about two or three hundred yards from the shore, before we found any branches worth taking all the way back to town. They were tough and only half dry, and as my axe was not nearly as sharp as the other boys' axes and I was not yet properly used to this job, I lagged far behind them. They could see at a glance the kind of branch that was to be stripped off, and they might have been professional lumber-jacks the way they lopped the branches and cut them into suitable lengths. All this I had yet to learn. After a couple of hours' hard work, when they had collected a big enough pile, they started carrying the wood down to the beach, and of course I had to do the same. At first, they pretended not to see the pitifully small amount I had gathered, but when the branches had been loaded into the boat and my heap looked childishly little by comparison, they suddenly felt sorry for me.

"Let's all go back into the forest," the elder brother said, "and we'll each bring as much as we can carry."

When we returned to the beach after about half an hour, my share of the boat's "deck cargo" had increased consider-ably.

We now took out our sandwiches, and I would have had time to gaze into the distance and listen to what the salt breezes blowing from there had to tell. But I had completely forgotten such things; I was as hungry as a wolf cub and could think of nothing but food.

After our meal we went swimming. The water in this

shallow, warm, sandy inlet was much the same as that of our own beach, perhaps a little colder. We splashed about for a long time, and my playmates showed me all the secrets of the art of swimming. I stood staring in admiration at all their tricks, and no wonder, for both of them later became famous swimmers.

The tiredness caused by our work had made me forget about gazing into the distance and listening to the sea. And this always happened on later trips as well. Every morning I set off refreshed from a good night's sleep and agog with expectation, and the island forest swallowed me up in hard work before I really knew what I was looking for.

On the way back there was never a sound. The boat was low in the water and rocked as slowly as the wave moving beneath it. The rowers needed all their strength to pull at the oars, and the helmsman did his work in silence. Our skin no longer felt the breeze from afar and made us think of the distance; our minds were on the everyday but imminent dangers around us.

When we got back to our own beach, the boat had to be pulled right up and washed clean every day. After that began the heaviest part of the work—carrying the load of firewood to our own cellars. The walk home from the beach was even longer than that from the clearing in the forest down to the boat, and it was already late in the afternoon. A crowd of women always collected in the yard of our house to admire the result of our efforts and to hint that, thanks to all this nice firewood, next winter would be much more cozy for us than the previous winters. But we said nothing. Later, the other boys confessed that after these excursions they were always very tired, but every evening their father paid them a wage. I got no pay. Usually I threw myself full length on the grass of the yard, went inside to eat the supper that Mother had made, and went back to the yard. Sprawling about like this I experienced something new: The gates were opened into a void, where there was not a single thought, not a single fancy, not the smallest awareness of my surroundings, of the passing of time, or even of myself.

This too pleased me. Sometimes it pleased me more than reading my books. At moments of tiredness it was safer to dive into a void than to go off riding Indians' wild horses.

The weight I had put on at the summer colony soon vanished on these wood-gathering trips, and when school began I looked just as delicate as before. Instead of the tan from sun and sea wind, I took on a transparent pallor. The following year—I could not go to the colony until the end of the summer, and these excursions began as soon as school broke up—the sun and sea made no difference at all to my color. My skin merely began to glisten and to stretch tightly across my pale cheeks.

The rowing trips were preparation for work. They did my two companions good, toughening them up and making them as strong as the trees growing stubbornly on the rocks by the water. But they took something out of me. When the teacher took our class out into the woods one day to practice running along a forest track, he looked at me anxiously for a long time and after my run he called me over to him and listened to my chest like a doctor.

"What on earth's wrong with you?" he said. "You look most peculiar. You should go to the doctor. Your heart is not good."

Even my heart had to prepare for something unusual. Nevertheless, I liked the sea and I liked rowing. For two summers I set off on countless weekday mornings, not only in calm, sunny weather, but often on windy, gray mornings when foaming waves dashed against the shore. Although they never had time to speak to me of those things that I so eagerly expected every morning, when evening came and I was tired they led me into a void in which I was content.

The last summer before I left school, something extraordinary happened to me. It had nothing to do with my fishing or wood-gathering trips or my stay at the summer colony, and not even the sun could make the summer green. Perhaps the black shadow of World War I was already having an effect on the events of that time? At any rate, numbers of unemployed began to appear in the town—the first I had ever heard of— and I saw them loafing about even on weekdays. Life also became more difficult for those who still worked as usual.

What really happened that summer? Probably the disturbances threatening our community appeared only as omens just then and affected only small groups, since few people stop to remember that time. But I cannot forget it. I can't describe just what we went through, yet I must pause for a moment at this stage of our journey, not so much to recall the past in the usual way as to listen to voices heard from some unknown region.

Perhaps I can best explain what I mean by trying to tell of a certain Sunday. I've no idea whether it was then the early or the late part of the summer or whether the summer was at its height. In any case, this particular day was fine and sunny.

In the morning I went off with my fishing rod down to the water, as I had done on summer mornings for many years. For some reason, however, I had no wish to spend the whole day there—perhaps hunger made me restless—and I soon went home. When I got back my parents stared at me inquiringly and my brothers rushed up to me, but having heard that I had caught nothing my mother and father lapsed into silence and the boys returned to their games.

We spent the whole of this day out of doors. Mother and Father lay full length in the middle of the yard, beside the path that sloped gently up to the outhouse. The grass was best

148

here, but there were also thick clumps of nettles. At that time it was the favorite meeting place for all the tenants. At meal-times on weekdays and in the evenings the men would collect there for a chat, and you would see women there at other times of the day. This day, others besides ourselves were there and the conversation turned to the unexpected slump in jobs. One person knew that such and such a stoneworker was out of work, another had heard that a certain carpenter had lost his job, a third said that a couple of other skilled workers were now at loose ends. Everyone was rather worried, and no doubt a little depressed, as each of the unemployed men lived near by. People came and went the whole time; after chatting for awhile they would go back to their chores or lie down for a nap. But our parents didn't move. When others were present they too tried to join in the conversation, but left on their own again they were silent. No one could know that we had had nothing whatever to eat that day.

Why had things taken such a bad turn for us? We children did not know the reason and we were given no explanation. We had been short of all kinds of things for years, but we had never known such a miserable day as this before. We were not only disappointed and hungry, but also bewildered. We could not explain to ourselves properly why Mother today made no attempt to go inside and get us something to eat.

The youngest child, the little girl, had been crawling around near our parents the whole time, looking for sorrel to put in her mouth, sometimes even cramming it with sand and dirt until Mother snatched her into her arms for a moment and wiped her face and mouth. About midday, when others kept being called to dinner, she fell asleep and Mother carried her inside. She herself didn't stay long, but came out and sat down in the same spot where she had been all morning.

I flung myself on my back beside Father as soon as I got home from the beach and didn't move until towards evening.

My brothers, on the other hand, ran about the whole morning with the others and only came over now and then to see whether anything to eat had appeared. But when the others went home for dinner, they too sat down near us in silence. The sun warmed us that day in an enervating sort of way, and the warm smell of the earth too seemed very tiring. All we could do was to stare ahead of us and hope that sleep would take us into its own good world.

But the only one it bothered about just then was our small sister. Usually on Sundays Father would have an afternoon nap; but when I stole a look at him now I saw that he was wide awake. While the other families were inside having their dinner, Mother was very restless. She tossed and turned and kept uttering soft little moaning sounds. But Father lay the whole time without moving, like a tree cut down and left to rot, his hands under his head and his gaze fixed on the one spot in the sky. Up on high that day there was not the faintest wisp of cloud to be seen, and I couldn't imagine what it was he saw there.

This first day of hunger did not bring any severe physical pains with it. These came later, a gift of the Great War. We just lay about now, quiet and wondering and listless.

As others appeared again in the yard my brothers left us. I noticed that they tried to run, throw stones, or climb trees the same as usual, but they had very little spirit or energy. Now and then they stood quite still as though to ponder some secret, and sometimes they even had to sit on the ground and watch the others running about. Their aim had not the accuracy or strength of their better days, and they did not show their customary daring and skill in climbing. But the others didn't seem to notice. I was glad of that. For some reason I wanted our secret to remain in our keeping for as long as possible.

Father's few attempts at conversation ceased completely

after dinnertime; when grownups began to stop beside us once more, he merely replied to their questions with a short grunt. I was not even sure whether he heard what they said. But Mother tried with a desperate brightness to take part in the conversations and to give them her own particular color. I had noticed before that there was often a touch of humor in what Mother said, but never had she been able to provoke such hearty laughter in her listeners as on that first Sunday when we were so hungry. In the light of her words the life of us all, the things that happened to us, and the whole world in which we lived, began to seem so comic that no one could take it seriously.

The afternoon seemed much longer than the morning; but as nothing particular happened to us, the hours slipped past even more dream-like than those of the forenoon. Or perhaps it should be said that for these hours we had been enclosed in a vacuum in which the passing of time could not be measured. Our little sister woke up, and when Mother brought her out into the yard again she went on as before eating sorrel and dirt, though more tearfully than in the morning. The boys broke off more frequently from their running and climbing and for longer periods. Father's grunts grew less audible, and Mother's sallies became sharper and shriller. But in a vacuum such things had no life or meaning, and they did not affect us at all. They were merely a kind of reflection of our earlier existence.

After a little more gossip, the housewives went inside again. Smoke began to drift out of their chimneys, and half an hour later they called their husbands in to afternoon coffee. Then they all came and chatted away to us again before going inside to get supper ready. But we stayed on in our vacuum, in which there was neither food nor passing of time, only the reflection of times gone by and the sharpening pangs of hunger.

151

Evening was already drawing on and the sun was sinking towards the forests that surrounded us Finns on all sides, when an old woman who had not been near us all day came laboriously down her steps into the yard and hobbled straight across to Mother.

"Look here now, Iita, haven't you had anything to eat all day long?" she asked.

Father gave an uneasy start, and Mother stared at the old woman for a moment with wild eyes and then burst into tears. The woman shook her head and turned to the others in the yard. "I've been watching from my window all afternoon and I can see they're hungry," she said. "Each of you now give them something to eat. I've got nothing."

She turned slowly, hobbled over to her steps and back into her room as laboriously as she had come.

Who was this woman? From my store of memories I can only find this one picture of her. Before this incident she had never approached us in any way, nor did she again after it.

For a long time the only sound in the yard was Mother's loud sobbing. At last Father got up and walked as though in shame towards our door, dragging his paralyzed leg behind him more slowly than usual. Not until he got to our steps did a woman say quietly, "Have you really had nothing to eat all day?"

And a young mother said, "Haven't your children had anything either?"

Mother could not answer them immediately, for the sobbing overcame her as it drew out the pain from deep inside her. For that reason I never knew what she answered. The second I heard those words I jumped up and rushed after Father, driven by the same shame as he to get out of people's sight. We were ashamed of our helplessness, our inability to support ourselves.

152

Inside, Father was sitting in his rocking chair, tipping it to and fro more violently than usual. I sat down by the window and stared out. The whole evening I saw nothing except the dark clouds slowly gathering in the sky.

For about a quarter of an hour there was complete silence all around us. Then we heard Mother come up the steps into the porch, take something from our pantry, and go out again. About ten minutes later she appeared in the porch again and came in with the milk can and a loaf of bread in her hand and all the children round her.

VII

I began my last year at the elementary school in the same way as the former years. The boy that walked by himself now left the world of sea and river for the world of the prairies and mountains and oceans and all the savage tribes. The need of books became so intense that those in the school library no longer sufficed. Somehow or other I had to wangle a few coppers and penetrate the much larger municipal library. I had to swallow bigger and bigger mental doses so that the wretched material portions could not force me to reflect on my real position, and with this goal ahead of me my wobbly heart had to work at full speed.

While Father on more and more evenings mended my more and more badly worn shoes, I had to start chopping wood in his stead and splitting up into firewood for the stove the odd bits of wood used in blasting at his place of work. And while Mother spent more and more time mending my ragged clothes, I had to take over her job of carrying fresh water inside and emptying the slops outside. But in spite of all this I had to have more and more to read, more and more books.

For all I knew, goodness and beauty had already vanished

153

from my life. My last Christmas was forgotten, gone from my consciousness. Nothing was left but forests and prairies, mountains and oceans, and South Sea Islands.

But now and again during the winter I was touched by something from quite a new direction.

Suddenly I felt I had to leave all the other books and start reading the only book the family possessed—a large, thick Bible, yellow with age. I've no idea why this happened. I only remember that I had to leave everything else. Somehow I got through the duties imposed by school and home, but there was no more tobogganing or taking part in snowball fights. For a time I even broke completely with the boys living in the same house. Every spare moment I spent poring over the thick book. As always, I had to start reading right from the beginning; and as this book was not easy to understand, it required a lot of thought. I could often devour an adventure story in a single evening, but it took much hard mental work for a boy of twelve to understand this book.

The lone runner suddenly had to stop and ponder why he was running and where he was going.

The rather meager Bible history lessons at school always had to be learned by heart, but only now did the people and the events I had read about begin to live and I saw them in a new light. Instead of good and evil, there was faith and the surrender of faith—the ever-recurring tragedy from one generation to the next. The earth, on whose yield man lived, had been made by the hand of the Creator, just like heaven, to which all hopes were directed.

In the Bible history book was a picture in which God, the Creator and Ruler of all things, had been given human form. Earlier, this had seemed natural. But as the events of the Bible came to life and rolled forward in all their immensity and even the greatest human destinies, when set against eternity, became insignificant, it was difficult to imagine the Creator as being like them. Even Solomon had felt this: "But will God indeed dwell on the earth? Behold, the heaven and heaven of heavens cannot contain thee; how much less this house that I have builded?"

The twelve-year-old too had to reject the picture in the Bible history and, like Solomon, believe that the form of God is inconceivable. Sometimes he would shut the book quickly and go to the window, looking out into the dark or at the winter sky lit by the stars. He felt that something was about to happen to him and he waited for it. But for some reason his expectation was never fulfilled, and he had to hurry back to the book, more eager than ever. There was no one with whom he could have talked about this matter. Father, and Mother too, had given up reading the Bible long ago. Their thoughts lurched about blindly in their need and distress. Here, too, the lone wanderer had to be alone.

Or perhaps he had to be alone because, as a twelve-year-old, he could no longer believe in the teacher's explanations of Bible history and already knew without asking that Mother's and Father's explanations would have seemed even stranger to him. The spirit of the school Bible history was gentle, but the spirit of the thick old Bible was stern and strong. Mother's and Father's minds neither knew nor were capable of grasping anything to which they could not give an everyday form, but the mind of the lone one was proud—far too proud—and he believed that one day he would stumble on the truth, the irrevocable truth.

He believed more in himself than in anything else, so his expectations could not come true. He did not know how to be humble.

This struggle lasted for perhaps two or three months. Driven on by some powerful inward urge, I had to read the Bible from beginning to end and to think, fiercely and stubbornly, about the innumerable things appearing in it.

155

During those months I changed outwardly as well. In my speech I began to use a new kind of language, so that both the teacher and my parents noticed it. In that way, too, I wanted to become better than before, to rise higher. On my way to school I could no longer run, I had to walk slowly, sunk deep in thought. I may have borrowed my new way of speaking and walking from the teacher, but it was not mere copying. The changes and struggles taking place within me made themselves visible even in my outward being.

The pallor of the lone wanderer in his threadbare clothes was already known, but it now turned to a sickly gray color which upset people who saw it. The teacher was very worried —it was he who had listened to my heart and realized there was something wrong with it—and told me several times that I was in a bad way. But most of all it frightened Mother.

"You're not to stay inside the whole time reading, you must go out sometimes too," she said. "Otherwise you'll die soon."

I paid no attention to her. I listened only to the voices awakening inside me. And they told me to read the Bible and try to understand what it contained.

But the proud could never understand that book. When I had read its last pages many times, I had to close the book hopelessly and my mind was overcome by a frightening desolation. Suddenly, deep down inside me, there was an utter void. For many an evening I sat by the window staring at the sky, trying desperately to hold on to hope and expectation, but they too had vanished. While reading the book, I had the feeling that I was about to be fulfilled with something new; this feeling had left me the moment the book was closed.

I was freed from this new ordeal of mine just as unexpectedly as I had been forced a few months earlier to leave all my other books and all my other thoughts and hopes. Perhaps I had not been found sufficiently good or competent, and for this reason I had to be left for a long time to face ordeals of another kind. Having spent several evenings at the window staring at the sky, I had to return slowly to my former interests. The runner must resume his endless running. The last few months before finishing school I had to go once more every Saturday to get something to read from the school library and with the few coppers I could come by I got more books every Sunday from the big municipal library. I had to try to forget what was happening inside me.

As though foreshadowing the war, a sharp battle was fought during these weeks between the boys in our part of town and the boys living at the end of Korkeavuorenkatu. We were fighting for possession of the hill on which the water tower was being built, and the battle went on for many weeks, until our side got help from the Gutzeit Company's boys. These were joined by a fifteen-year-old with a miniature rifle. When he had fired it several times, the enemy fled and the field was ours.

The solitary one also took part in this fight, and it was this which brought him slowly out of his void, closer to others of his own age and to the everyday reality in which he too had to live. He did not get rid of his loneliness, but he was now able to throw himself into the company of others if only for a while.

CHAPTER FIVE

I

When school broke up and the teacher gave us our final reports, I noticed for the first time that it was spring and that the buds on the trees had just burst and the grass was beginning to turn green. I also felt very proud on this occasion because I was wearing a brand-new and gleaming white shirt. Where it had come from I can't remember.

As we began to disperse, the teacher called me over to him. "Would you like to go on to secondary school, if I arranged for you to be exempt from paying tuition?" he asked.

I looked past him into the far distance and shook my head. "I can't. I must leave school and look for work."

"I don't suppose things are easy for you with your father ill. But think the matter over until the autumn."

To me the secondary school seemed such a strange place that I dreaded it. The boys and girls who went to it, and their parents, were different people from us. Not for a moment did I dare to think of mixing with them.

The hungry must think only of work.

That day I showed off in my new shirt, and my mother stood nearly all day in the yard, leaning against our front door and boasting to everyone of the excellent school report her eldest boy had. If anyone stopped to listen to her, tears filled her eyes—to my shame—as she told how many top marks I had received and what a clever boy I was. For some reason she was not working anywhere that day.

But the very next morning I put on my shabbiest clothes and set off with two other boys for the loading wharf of the Gutzeit lumberyard in search of work. Small Estonian schooners, which carried mostly shingles and staves, could come right up beside the stacked timber. There I began my actual work and earned my very first wages.

For several weeks it seemed to me that my life had reached the bottom of the abyss and had begun to climb upwards towards the heights.

I was then almost thirteen. At first my back ached and time seemed to pass very slowly, but otherwise I was content to be working. I imagined that the money I earned would gradually alter the course of my whole life. The job itself did not greatly please me; there were nothing but women and children all around me, and the strange way the women talked and squabbled irritated me from the start. But I tried to close my ears to it all, and in the dinner break one of my friends whose father worked as carrier in the lumberyard, would set off to show us the curiosities of this big place. We saw small, narrow-gauge trains with their wagons in endlessly long lines, laden with planks and other timber, puffing from one part of the huge yard to the next. We climbed on the decks of tugs hissing with steam and peered down into the dark caverns of the engine rooms. We clambered up the tarred sides of squat barges and saw the vast amount of wood they could carry in their insides. Sometimes we ran to the sawmill to watch how the logs, guided by the lumbermen, floated up to the hoist, were seized by its sharp teeth, rose dripping from the water, and vanished, creaking and groaning, inside the mill. We never dared follow them as far as that, for when our guide's father was not working there it was better for us to keep outside.

Close to it was a still bigger industrial plant, a cellulose factory, but it looked so frightening that we were content to look at even its outside walls from afar. Its pungent smell, which sometimes spread all over the city, hung over it with stifling heaviness day and night, and its dirty black walls, its rows of gloomy, staring windows, and the clouds of steam and smoke belching out of it were sufficiently alarming even from a distance. Not until I grew up did I become better acquainted with the cellulose factory.

The working day was still ten hours at that time. When I got home in the evening I drank the coffee Mother had made and threw myself down on the bed to rest. When supper was ready I moved over to the table for a while. Mother would then unfold the beds, and when I had eaten all I could, I got undressed, crawled under the quilt, and fell into a deep sleep. When the summer was a little more advanced and the water a little warmer, I spent my evenings differently. After coffee I usually went down to the beach for a swim; then I would lie in the sun until I thought supper was ready. As soon as I had eaten, I went to bed.

I learned about loading ships and I saw all kinds of new things. Books and boyish games suddenly vanished from my life. During those days and weeks I thought very little, but inside me expectation lived again, a new anticipation. I imagined that perhaps I too could now begin to live like other people.

160

When the ship was loaded, we usually were given two or three days off and a small sum of money from our wages to tide us over. Then we would walk about the town. We wanted to become familiar with the grownups' world and to understand it better and better. Many things which before had seemed absurd and strange to us had suddenly begun to excite our intense curiosity. Sometimes we sat down in front of a kiosk, bought a bottle of lemonade and a bun, and tried to listen to and watch what was being said and done around us. Having spent our money on this amusement—it only lasted for two or three times—we mostly frequented places where grownups gathered, like the marketplace, the docks, the building sites, and the front of the workers' hall. We felt we were beginning to belong to these circles, though of course no one looked on us as grown men. People smiled at us kindly, but at the same time in a rather superior and puzzling way.

We wanted to become like the men who were wearing clothes bought with their own money and who had food bought with their own wages in their stomachs.

During those weeks the lone wanderer forgot all about the prairies and the oceans and the struggle with the Bible.

When we went back to load another Estonian schooner we almost felt like skilled workers. My cheeks took on a healthier color and the muscles of my arms grew stronger. My stomach, which had troubled me for a long time, got much better. My faith in my growing success became firmer and firmer. I imagined that I had left all my misfortunes behind me and that I could now make myself into what I really wanted to be. I should be able to help my whole family, raise it from its misery to the level of our neighbors and perhaps even higher.

I imagined every day reality to be just as childish as the world of imagination, but for many weeks I was happy and I helped to load three or four boats.

When my backache was better and my body got used to the

work, I became such a hard worker that even the shrill-voiced women in the hold took a liking to me, though I didn't like them at all. I couldn't get used to their language, but I managed to shut my ears to them. Though I had lost the prairies and the oceans and almost forgotten my struggle with the Bible, there was still something inside me that made me a misfit.

I knew nothing of the dark shadow that was threatening the whole civilized world. We had no newspapers at home. The approaching war was talked about down at the docks, I suppose, but the lone wanderer had shut his ears even to these conversations. When his body was at work his mind was dreaming in its own void, and when his body was at rest his mind was eagerly building itself a road that led to prosperity.

II

On the 28th of July, which happened to be my day off, I was walking about the town by myself for some reason. I didn't notice anything special; work was going on everywhere as usual, and being alone I didn't dare to go and listen to what the groups of men were saying. But on my way back to our part of the town I suddenly heard words which startled me. Two young men, whom I knew by sight, were standing at the corner of Katariina Square talking excitedly. I heard them say that war had broken out and was threatening to spread among all the great powers.

I knew nothing of the events of the past few days and so did not quite understand the situation, but in some way I was upset. I could not understand what war it was that had been threatening us for a long time. What did those great powers want of each other? I had known about all kinds of wars and battles from books, but it had never occurred to me that nations in our age would still start killing each other. That very day, however, living men had been shot and others were being shot at that moment. And to my amazement some people had been expecting and dreading this event for a long time.

When the men parted I ran as fast as I could to our own yard. I imagined that I now had alarming news to tell everybody. But I was quite mistaken. Everyone already knew much more about the war than I did. The whole yard was in ferment. Boys were telling each other strange tales of emperors and generals and armies fighting on the borders of their countries. Women in a tight cluster were wondering excitedly what was going to happen to all of us. The games of the small boys had suddenly taken on an entirely new tone; various bits of wood were being used as guns and they were being fired just as eagerly as I had once fired the gun given to me for Christmas and so soon broken.

The lone wanderer, blind and deaf, found that even in these homes the war had been expected and dreaded for a long time.

In the evening I heard remarks exchanged at home too:

Mother: "I wonder how it will affect us . . . perhaps we had better leave this place and go right into the country somewhere."

Father: "It won't touch us."

Mother: "They say that the Germans are going to land here."

Father: "They're no worse than any other foreigners."

Next morning I went down to the loading wharf as usual, but the expected schooner had not arrived, and one or two said they had heard that it never would. The docks were suddenly half-empty. Warships were now cruising about at sea.

So perhaps I would have no more chance at a good square meal bought with money I had earned myself.

For several days I wandered about the town with my

friends looking for a new job and listening to the news. We had to find out what was happening. At least once a day we stopped in at the reading room of the town library to read the newspapers. The war was spreading rapidly, as had been expected, and the armies that had suddenly collected began their gigantic battles. The accounts in the papers made it clear even to the most stupid of us that things very different from those we had read about in books were now happening, and all the rumors, like tangled gray skeins, made our daily life still more confused. I felt as if I too were being sucked by some mysterious power into the vortex of mighty events.

The search for work grew more and more hopeless day by day. The old flourishing trades dwindled and dwindled, until they puckered up like punctured balloons. Whole families, alarmed by rumors, began to leave town and move out to the country and the farms from which they had originally come. The poorer families loaded their belongings on railway wagons, and the richer ones sold off their houses at half-price. The pace of life, instead of slowing down, grew more hectic, seeking desperately for new forms of expression to replace those that were disappearing. Russian troops appeared, and an artillery division was quartered in the field near our house.

It began to dawn on me that my career as a laborer had been broken off suddenly after only a few weeks. My hopes and dreams had been shipwrecked. Instead of success, I began to feel in my very body that we were being besieged by new miseries, that a shadow more dismal and inconceivable than before was about to cover us. Even Mother, who had tried to get work down at the docks, had to stay at home now; and although we children were growing and needed more to eat than ever, food got less and less day by day.

Tired of our aimless running about, my friends and I began to take an interest in the soldiers billeted near our homes, inspecting them in our own particular way and puzzling over the riddle of their presence there. Often we climbed onto the fence and even tried to talk to them. In some way or other we always managed to make out a word or two, and gradually we began to understand them so well that we could form bits of sentences. This made the Russians take notice. At first they ignored us, merely shouting something as they walked past, but when they began to understand us a few of them stopped to talk. They wanted to know who we were, what our fathers did, what we knew about the war, and we answered as well as we could.

Thanks to one of my pals, our conversations about the war once took a dangerous turn. His parents were of the opinion that the Russians would soon be trounced by the Germans, and he repeated this from the top of the fence in no uncertain terms. The Russians were so angry that we had to make our escape and hide. Fortunately they did not look very far for us, and it was not long before we had been forgotten and could perch on the fence once more.

Since, in the early days, the soldiers could not eat all the food in the field kitchen that stood steaming at the edge of the woods, the cook offered the leftovers to us. At first only very few of us dared to seize this chance. The Russians' buckwheat porridge and cabbage soup smelled so temptingly good, however, that half-starved people like us licked our lips; yet most of us would not go and get dishes which could have been filled. The food was Russian, and the events of the general strike were still fresh in our memory. The Russian tsar was our enemy, and it was shameful to take bread from his hand. But after a time this patriotic objection began to fade. Day by day more and more people collected round the field kitchen, some almost ashamed, others quite brazen. The cook was a pleasant fellow with a sense of humor, and hungry stomachs yearned for the crumbs that fell from the imperial table.

For a long time Father saw to it that we were among the

resisters. The former stoneworker, paralyzed and exhausted by his fight for life, tried to hold out among the proud and respected patriots. Mother thought differently right from the start. In her view it was wiser to get a good square meal, even if the food was despised, than to go hungry in order to preserve some meaningless sense of honor. While nations waged war for the mastery of the world, we were fighting over porridge and the respect of dignified citizens. Father stood his ground successfully for several weeks, but at last he had to give in. It happened, I think, on an evening more hungry than usual.

One evening, at any rate, Mother joined the soup line with her can, and Father too ate Russian cabbage soup.

After that Mother would have gone every evening to stand in line, but the situation soon changed. The queue soon grew so long that there was not enough of the soldiers' food to go around. The cook tried to help by giving smaller portions to each person, but, even so, more and more were left without. And suddenly the whole game was at an end. From some high quarter came the stern order that the soldiers' food was not to be given to civilians. And a military guard with a rifle was posted to make sure that the civilian population kept away from the field kitchen.

My pals and I watched this spectacle from the top of the fence, but when the food supply stopped, our interest in the Russians faded anyway. We already knew them well enough, and all the other events of the war were losing their freshness. We didn't bother to climb on the fence any more, but went back to exploring our old paths into the forest and down to the beach. Having found no work despite our efforts, we were almost forced to become just boys again.

But we still remained in the grip of a certain uneasiness. Often when we were in the woods we would see Finnish women out walking with Russian soldiers. Fathers and young men in the prime of life would disappear, having taken work at the Russian batteries along the coast and out in the archipelago. The metal factories began making almost nothing but ammunition or other war materials. Although the news in the papers no longer was as interesting, we boys were in a state of constant restlessness.

I had forgotten the secrets of fishing. And both my wood-gathering companions from the summer were at work. Their wide-awake father had secured places for them as apprentices. As I walked about with my new friends, I began to think once more about books.

When the schools started, Mother asked me whether, despite our difficulties, I would not try to get into the secondary school, where the teacher had promised to help me. I shook my head. During the aimless wandering of the summer, my dread of the secondary school had increased rather than diminished. On my last free days I rushed about desperately looking for a job of some kind. I was like a drowning man clutching at a straw. But when no work could be found, I was put at a boys' trade school.

III

I have a very vague recollection of the latter phases of World War I. Most of them have been forgotten completely. There were a few bright moments when I found work for short periods; over everything else spread a misery which was gloomier than ever. Perhaps those brief moments of pleasure were provided so that the lonely one could now and then rest in the light and muster his strength to walk his dark road to the end.

During those years my ego was disciplined so severely that it has never been the same since, nor has it ever resembled that of healthy people.

And at the school where I was put that autumn I did very badly. The teachers were an engineer and an architect. Their teaching methods, as well as the subjects they taught, differed somewhat from the elementary school, but I don't think this was the only reason why the pupil who had been given such a good report in the spring suddenly found himself at the bottom of the class. Even to this day I can't quite explain the real reason. All I know is that the shadow of want and distress had become noticeably darker. I can recall odd glimpses and events of those days, but when I try to put them into any kind of order, anguish jumbles my thoughts.

In the school workshop I was an even greater failure than in the classroom, although the teacher there was a gifted turner with more than the ordinary education. He set us first of all to learn the rudiments of forging and filing. From a small piece of iron we were supposed to forge and file a right-angled base, saw a hole in one end, and into this solder one side of an important tool. I never managed to finish this first specimen of skill. The others progressed as filers and turners of increasingly difficult objects and took turns spending a few days in the foundry to learn the duties of a metal molder. For perhaps two or three months the teacher tried to make me keep up with the others, but when he saw that my right angle did not show any signs of completion and when a whole day spent at the lathe yielded the same poor result, he at last transferred me permanently to the foundry. There, all kinds of dirty work could be found even for a duffer.

Fortunately, the teacher in the foundry, an elderly molder, took a liking to me, perhaps out of pity, and this often consoled me on my dark days.

When I grew up I became a smith—quite a good one, in fact—at a younger age than usual, so that it is not easy to explain the humiliation of my early years as being due to a lack of practical ability.

168

This first winter of the war Father was still working as usual, and Mother worked as a washerwoman. Two grownups were employed, that is, yet the scarcity of food and other essentials haunted us as never before. Perhaps the wages for day laborers had been lowered, perhaps there was less washing to be had, or perhaps the need of food for us children was now so great that the week's rations were all eaten up in two or three days.

When she had fed us and got us to bed, Mother would start mending our clothes every evening by sewing patches made from strips of old clothes on top of the former patches. Because of their age, these patches were so weak that they often tore the very next day. Somehow or other Mother managed to keep her own clothes looking tolerable, but Father was no better off than we were in this respect. When his stoneworker's blouse had disappeared, he wore a coat that had probably been his Sunday best, in which, despite Mother's untiring efforts, one hole after the other appeared. Mother struggled valiantly, but she fought a losing battle.

Almost as often as Mother patched our clothes, Father would sit of an evening mending our worn-out shoes. The more his strength gave out, the less time he had left for sitting in his rocking chair. His offspring sucked their life force from his wasting blood. He still had his cobbler's hammer, last, and awl, but could very seldom afford to buy new leather. His work was as hopeless and depressing as Mother's.

My memory has little to tell about these days when we sank deeper and deeper into poverty. It merely lays bare the facts about our affliction.

There was also a constant shortage of firewood. I had not gone to the island to gather wood the previous summer, and nowadays Father brought home from work much smaller pieces than before. Perhaps he could carry only small loads, perhaps there was a new rule that not even broken blocks and boards were to be taken away from the working site. I don't know the reason, but to add to the increasing darkness it became more and more difficult for us to light the stove.

When I got home from school I often had to go into the forest and trudge through the snow with a sack over my shoulders looking for dry branches to break off the trees so that I could start the fire in our stove. At that time, taking wood like this was forbidden and more or less illegal, but I had to tempt fate and commit this offense many times every week.

Sometimes in the evenings, when darkness covered our intent, Mother and I went out together. We took the axe and sled and disappeared out on the bog. As the Russian artillery soldiers quartered next door to us had already been sent off to the front in the autumn, complete silence reigned at this time of night in the woods. On the drained bogland alders grew, and it was easier to deal with them than with birches and pines. One alder made two or three sledloads of firewood; admittedly it was green, but thanks to it we could keep away from the dangerous forest for several days.

If it did not snow during the night, everyone moving about there next morning noticed at once that a bigger crime had been committed than the breaking off of branches. But as the marks of the sled runners ended in a public road, it was not easy to pin the crime onto any one person; and, besides, ordinary people had no wish to start interfering in matters of this kind. Only if they suspected the offender to be an enemy might they try to have him punished; but we had no enemies. We had excellent proof of this whenever anyone stopped in to see us. The top of the baking oven and the stove was nearly always piled with green bits of alder slowly drying, and the unmistakable smell filled the whole room. The callers might glance at the wood, but they never asked any questions. They wanted to know as little as possible about our secret in case they might have to give evidence against us.

Our life was hard. But was our increasing poverty the only cause of the deeper and deeper spiritual darkness of this time?

Now and then I went to the reading room of the city library to see what was happening in the world; but if I were to try now to recall what was in the papers, I should have to read them again. My memory tells me nothing, not a word. I had begun to borrow books again and made desperate attempts to escape from reality. Sometimes in the evenings when Father went to the cellar to look at his almost nonexistent haul of wood and Mother had gone out somewhere, I would poke about in odd corners and occasionally find a few coppers. That winter they were about the only money I had with which to borrow books. Father never complained that his tobacco money had vanished; perhaps he guessed who the pilferer was and forgave him. But the books borrowed with that money never brought me goodness or beauty.

One Sunday, however, there appeared among them a book which aroused my imagination. It so happened that the library had not a single one of the adventure stories I wanted. At random I ordered a book called *Isle of the Happy Ones*. Perhaps the name attracted me—I knew nothing of the author at that time—but when it was handed to me I was disappointed at first by its small size. I should have gotten more reading matter with my pilfered money. But having ordered it, there was nothing I could do but take it home with a heavy heart.

From the very first the book began to excite me in quite a new way. I can remember nothing whatever of the story, but I cannot forget what it did to me. The events it described carried me far away from my own home and from my town; yet the book did not let me forget them for a second. On the contrary, it made me look at them in a new light. It reminded me every moment that if I wanted to be free from the poverty and misery in which I lived, I would have to leave the present and the past behind me and set off to make "an isle of the happy ones" somewhere else, perhaps far away.

At first I had been searching eagerly for a gateway through which I could pass, leaving reality outside the world of books. The *Isle of the Happy Ones* would then have been good to have, perhaps even better than Indians on the prairies or pirates on the high seas. But this book knew nothing of such a gateway. On the contrary, the wanderer in the dark was reminded at every step that Mother was sitting beside him patching his torn trousers, Father was mending shoes and, on days of intense cold outside, all the other children were indoors and crawling about the floor. The smell of the drying alders pricked his nostrils with every breath he took. And in his stomach the pains, which every day for a long time now had been twisting and turning, griped more severely than ever. The strange book never let him forget reality for a moment. On the contrary, this was the one thing it forced him to look at and think of.

I usually read a small book like this in an hour or two, but this one I had to read the whole afternoon and until late in the evening. I had to leave off to stare in front of me, look about me, watch Mother tearing tiny pieces from small bits of rag to use as patches for equally ragged clothes, Father stitching hopelessly rotten bits of leather on top of old patches in our shoes, and the children romping on the floor in shamefully ugly scraps of clothing. I could do nothing but sit on at the table reading the same passages over and over again. I found no peace. In the midst of thoughts trying to escape other thoughts kept waking—strange, restless thoughts which never allowed me to forget even in sleep.

I made a note at once of this author's name. Not until later did I read of his death in an old newspaper and find out the kind of man he had been. Then I knew that for a long time I had been breathing the same air as he. But, in my darkness, I was not then able to appreciate his books properly.

Every day I could forget, in my own way, that I was hungry, that the wood burning in the stove and the books I was reading were stolen, and that I was the worst pupil in the class and fit for nothing but the foundry.

IV

At that time the metal trade was greatly respected. The front lines that were spreading all over Europe every day demanded more and more and better and better arms, and the governments paid handsome prices for them. With the coming of spring all the boys in the metal section of the trade school boasted that they already had jobs lined up. I too was given a respite to last the summer. With some other boys, I went to see the foreman of a small workshop nearby, and he promised to take us all on as soon as school broke up.

Father had left us. He had not died, and I can remember nothing about him except that he was no longer with us. I don't think I even went to see him wherever he was.

In the small workshop, which I think had previously acted mainly as a bicycle repair shop, were now several small machines which were used for making hasps and hinges for ammunition boxes. The boxes were made at a box factory, and the foreman of the workshop had been told he could go on making the hasps and hinges as fast as he could turn them out. It was still thought that there was enough iron even for articles of this kind.

All the other new machines had been put inside the workshop except two cutters, which had been left out in the yard. The big one cut the iron bars and sheets into different shapes and sizes. It severed and sliced everything fed into it. But the smaller cutter, which I was put in charge of, did nothing but bite off one corner of pieces that were a standard length and thickness. I don't remember who worked with me. Perhaps there were different people, though I stayed at my place the whole summer. I see myself by turns feeding pieces into the teeth of the machine and supplying power to the blades by means of a long shaft.

I was at work again. I was earning money and I could eat food I had bought myself. I can still remember, clearly and in detail, the greatest occasion for joy of the whole summer. When I brought my first wages home, Mother let me eat, all by myself, the small loaf of unleavened bread I had bought, thickly spread with butter, and drink as many cups of coffee as I wanted. Besides being extravagant, this was unwholesome food for a boy with a weak stomach. But I felt that Mother wanted to give me her blessing in her own particular way. She had come home from work at the same time as I had, and there was nothing to eat at home except what we had brought with us. She knew that the time she took to get supper ready would seem very long to her hungry son.

The machines inside pressed grooves and punched holes in the pieces of iron and bent them into shapes suitable for their purpose. On several nights in the early summer, when I was not very well known in the building and there was a great rush to get the goods finished, I had to work overtime. I was put in charge of the machine that punched the holes in the end of the hasps. On those nights I earned a lot of money, and this particular mark of favor was shown to me because the others who usually looked after these more complicated machines were so tired from having worked for several nights in a row that they had to have a night off to sleep. But even on these nights that brought me extra money I was reminded that the black shadow had not left me. The foreman came round two or three times late at night to inspect our work and each time he stopped beside me. He said nothing, but I could see from his face that he was not satisfied. I was unable to punch the holes in just the way I should have done. And the minute he got more boys for his workshop, he avoided putting me on night work even during rush periods. For set hours of the day I had to stand tending the machine that required the minimum of skill.

I sometimes felt that even my face was repulsive to the foreman. The others had not yet said anything about its sickly color, but he sensed that behind my face was hidden something which he better avoid as much as possible.

Fortunately such things affected me very little that summer. The whipped dog could rest and dream with a full stomach.

At the back of the workshop were two workmen, one a filer and the other a turner. The former was a tallish man and very talkative. When we lay on the grass in the yard during the lunch break he was always to be heard telling stories from the four corners of Finland. He had the old-time journeymen's blood in his veins and he had to obey its call even as a filer. He was getting on for fifty, but he could never stay in one place for very long, and he was proud of the fact that on his travels he had come to know his job inside out and had learned every trick of the trade. Whatever new knack had been invented, he had picked it up. And our foreman thought highly of him. But one day before the end of the summer he left us, and left town too, and went off in search of something new to learn somewhere else.

He never spoke to me. At lunch time all the others gathered round him ready to laugh at his endless stock of jokes, but I lay a little apart from the others and never laughed aloud at his stories, only smiled my pale smile. Sometimes he glanced at me, but always looked away quickly. When he had gone, the others soon forgot him, I was the only one to dream about him for a long time, and at happy moments I imagined I was traveling along with him somewhere far away on strange-looking highroads. Perhaps he would have spoken to me then, and I could have appreciated his stories better than by merely laughing at them.

The turner, on the other hand, was quite a different type. He asked nothing of life but work, and so his picture has faded from my mind. All I remember is that whenever anyone happened to glance into the workshop through the window on the street side, whether late in the evening or early in the morning, he always saw the turner busy at his lathe. We all knew that he had no other home but this workshop. For an hour or two during the night he would roll up on the floor beside his lathe, but as sleep seldom came, he got up and went on with his work as soon as dawn began to break.

The days and nights passed me by as in a dream. I heard about the events of the war and the affairs of the neighborhood, but they did not concern me. Sometimes in the evenings, as I lay almost naked in the sun at the swimming baths and glanced at the sky where the ever-changing clouds drifted past or across the sea to the horizon, I would remember what I had sometimes thought about beauty and goodness and the truth that rested above all, but even these now could not rouse me from my sleep. I merely existed, did my work, and ate the food I had earned. The restless thoughts born on the isle of the happy ones had vanished completely, but the wanderer was able to buy himself brand-new trousers and a new shirt. If he sometimes really wished something for himself, he hoped that one day he could join the filer on his travels along the distant highroads and listen to his stories.

Sometimes in the evenings at the swimming baths I met the boys with whom I had spent the previous summer loading the ships; but now we were bored with each other's company.

They too were working again somewhere and getting on very well. They often stopped to exchange a few words, as though to recall old days. But the winter was between us, and having looked at me for a few moments they suddenly fell silent and went away. And in one way I was pleased that they left me alone.

What pleased me most was that I could rest by myself, dream as if in a heavy sleep, and not remember anything of the past. I knew nothing of the present and had no hopes for the future other than that some day I might roam the far off, nameless roads.

As the evenings began to draw on, the Russian government suddenly found that iron was needed much more for ammunition than for the hasps and hinges of ammunition boxes, and our work came to an end. Then I had to wake up once more from my dream and set off again into the darkness.

V

When autumn came I had to go back to school. During lesson times it was hard to understand what the teachers said and explained; and in the workshop, I had to confine myself to the foundry, shovel piles of sand, carry coke, and in general do all the dirty work. Only occasionally was I allowed to melt iron and brass into a flowing substance that radiated intense heat and glowed yellow-red and white. The duffer could sometimes mold the patterns for simple objects out of sand, but not even this year was he thought capable of turning and filing.

In the evenings I had to slink into the forest again to steal wood, as the earnings with which I had been able to get a new shirt and a new pair of trousers were not enough for buying logs. My trips into the forest had to be made more often than the previous winter, since there were no bits of wood brought home by Father. The strong smell of melted mutton fat had left our room at the same time as Father. Perhaps our well-to-do neighbor had grown tired of mutton this winter. As the darkness and the autumn gales began to besiege us and the cold crept inside, hunger attacked us again, gleefully, sure of its victory.

Where could Father have been? Where could Mother have been working this winter? For a time she was probably at a place where they arranged emergency relief work in the form of making boots out of felt and rag.

Twice at least this winter she got half a sack of rye meal with a chit given her by the relief office. We dragged it home together from a shop on the sled.

Once I went myself to this solemn office where the supply of flour was granted or refused. Mother told me that you could often hear grown-up people weeping and uttering curses and cries of rage and distress; but when I entered the office I saw nothing like this. At that moment I was the only applicant there; the official on duty spoke kindly to me and put ten marks into my hand.

Where could Mother have been that day? Why did she send me there, and how is it I dared go inside the door? I was shy and I was more afraid of people than ever before.

This winter we sometimes had to go begging too. There were days when there was not a crust of bread in the larder and not a speck of flour in the sack. We three boys would then go out together. I was a kind of adviser to the others, as I never dared to put my nose inside a shop door and ask for food like a beggar. The middle boy plucked up his courage once or twice and got some bread from one or two shops, half a loaf and once even a whole loaf, but then he too felt so ashamed that he refused to go on. Begging children were smiled at in a way that was like a stab to the heart.

The most brazen and successful of us was the youngest; he

was still too small to know anything of shame and went straight into shops as many times as was necessary. Thanks to him we got more than one tasty loaf.

At one shop, kept by a bachelor, he never came away empty-handed. He became quite a favorite, in fact. When he was asked why he begged, he answered honestly:

"Daddy's ill and is not at home."

"When was he taken ill?"

"Next Monday."

All the customers laughed out loud; the shopkeeper himself laughed till his broad belly shook. Why, you couldn't help giving bread to a jolly lad like that. A whole loaf every time.

And we brought it home, divided it equally among the whole family, and ate it.

This winter Mother too was ill. One morning she could not get out of bed; she was panting and hot with fever. When I got home from school I had to go to the druggist for some powders—it so happened that day that we had just enough money—and with their help she tried to get up. It was no use; next morning her temperature had risen much higher. Then a neighbor went and reported the matter to a sister of charity at the relief office. When this woman called to see us for the first and last time, I chanced to be at home.

She stood by Mother's bed, asked her one or two questions, then pulled back the quilt and put a thermometer in her armpit. Mother's feverish eyes suddenly glowed with shame, and I too writhed in the grip of some unknown anguish. The quilt still looked fairly decent, though it had been patched many times, but beneath it a heap of broken straw was exposed which the remnants of a tattered mattress tried desperately to hide. There was not a sheet of any kind. These had all worn out long ago, except the one that had been carefully kept as a white cover for our pile of rags in the daytime.

Only when I saw the sister of charity staring at them, did I too feel ashamed of our wretchedness. She said nothing, however, and tried to banish the amazement from her face. Having taken Mother's temperature, she gave her some medicine from a small bottle which she left on the table. Then she said gently to Mother, "Take this medicine again today, and three times tomorrow—morning, midday, and evening. If your temperature doesn't go down, send your boy to me with a message and I'll come and see you again."

As she moved to the door she said, "I don't think you're seriously ill. It's just an ordinary fever."

Next day Mother got up. She was still shaky, but able to prepare a meal for us. And the day after that she went back to work. I didn't have to go with a message to the sister of charity, though the first night I had had a nightmare about it.

But a few days later I was surprised by a visit of quite a different kind. I had just come home from school and was alone when two ladies came in. They asked where my mother was, looked around them critically, and at first seemed rather disappointed. Their attention was drawn particularly to our one and only remaining sheet, which covered the sad remnants of our bedclothes.

"It doesn't look so bad here," the elder woman said.

"They even have sheets," said the younger one.

"I wonder what the sister of charity meant?"

At last one of them took hold of the sheet and pulled it off. Then they both understood what the sister of charity had meant and moved to the door.

"When your mother comes home from work this evening, tell her to come and see me," the elder woman said, and they disappeared as quickly as they had come.

The elder one had told me her name, and when Mother went to see her she was given two sheets and two pillow cases. When the sheets were stretched over the mattress they stopped the tiny bits of broken straw from being scattered over the floor, and the mattresses lasted longer than usual. Straw too cost money, so that it was difficult to buy a new mattress.

This winter all our neighbors began to notice that we were in a very bad way, and some of them said to Mother that our youngest children should be put in a children's home and that I should be made to work.

"It's ridiculous, that boy going to a trade school. Why, even our boys don't go."

Mother didn't answer such talk, but anyone who could read the expression on her face knew that she would never let her children away from her side as long as she lived. Perhaps she remembered how it felt to be sent to a strange family as a little girl. But she would sometimes look at me as though to say that my schooling *was* senseless.

Sometimes I went here and there asking for work. I went to the same small shop where I had worked the previous summer. I went for several mornings in a row to the gates of the biggest machine shop to wait for the foreman. I went and showed myself to the municipal building contractor, and I went to several other places as well, but all in vain. Everyone could read in my face what the foreman the previous summer had guessed. They glanced at me indifferently and shook their heads. I often had the feeling that when they saw my eyes, they wanted to forget all about me. My leanness and my ragged clothes perhaps might have passed, but my frightened eyes . . .

Mother too made an attempt now and then to ask about work for me. She realized that a boy from a family like ours couldn't hope for a place as errand boy in a shop or apprentice in a tailor's workshop, but somewhere surely they needed someone to chop wood or carry water or do odd jobs of that kind. Once she made a reckless effort and took me along to the kitchen of the house where the engineer of the machine shop lived. It was a fine, large kitchen and the maid was ironing her master's shirts with an electric iron, rare in those days. Mother spoke to her:

"Would you please ask your master to come here? I want to ask him if he will take on my boy at the machine shop."

The maid, a well-fed woman with a gleaming white apron, looked at us for a moment with a superior smile. Then she pulled the plug of the electric iron out of the wall and disappeared into an inner room. After a while she came back to the kitchen followed by the engineer.

My mother had also been a maid at one time, and at the proper moment she knew how to adapt her speech to that spoken in cultured circles. But now she was all confused, and instead of putting our case clearly and briefly she began to speak in a complaining, humble tone and to say anything but what she should have said. The engineer did not even bother to listen to her, but stared for a moment at my eyes. Then he held up his hand snubbingly and cut Mother short:

"We've no work at present," he said. "Perhaps later. Let the boy go along to the machine shop and apply for a position."

And he turned quickly and went inside. He too wanted to forget my frightened eyes immediately.

So we had to return home, and not a word did we say to each other on the way.

I don't think I read a single book that winter, and I did not see many newspapers either. I merely gasped with anguish and shame. I did not even hear about the events of the war until later.

Chapter Six

I

When the last dirty patches of snow vanished from the streets and people began cleaning around their houses more vigorously than ever, Father appeared home again from the hospital. By that time I was so scared that I didn't dare go even within calling distance of any place that might have offered charity, and I did not have the feeblest hope of ever getting a job. For his part, Father was strangely whitefaced and just as silent as ever. He sat rocking in his chair, now and then going outside to the edge of the woods, gazing at the course of the sun and perhaps deep in thought. At the meeting place in the yard he would have had to answer a lot of questions, and this he did not want. He wanted to be alone, sometimes even away from his family; and at the edge of the field where the Russian troops had been quartered at the outbreak of war, complete silence now reigned.

A silence that foreboded the surprising and alarming end of the war.

But one evening Father said to Mother, "I've heard that unemployed are now being taken on to crush stones for roads. The lad here can't do work like that yet, but if I go with him he'll soon learn."

I was touched to know that he was thinking of my future, and at the same time ashamed of my own wretched helplessness. I had already turned fourteen and had been to a boys' trade school.

Next morning Mother put some sandwiches and a bottle of milk into Father's old knapsack, and he and I set off. At last I was once more feeling a trifle hopeful. Father's words had untied the knot of a depression which had been choking me for a long time. I had no idea what Father was feeling deep inside.

We walked together through the town. Usually at this early morning hour you met people on their way to work on almost every street; but for the last few months a strange silence had begun to settle down over our town, the expectation of great events, the shadow of things unknown. When I saw only a few people hurrying past us, alone and not anxious to talk, I too wanted to get to our imagined place of work as quickly as possible. But because of Father I had to walk slowly. As soon as we got outside the gateway of our yard, I noticed that he dragged his leg much more than before this last illness. Although I had watched him for several days, I had not seen how lame he was. Only now, when I felt tied to him, was I forced to notice his shuffling gait.

As we approached the machine shop we saw that the workmen in their grimy overalls had formed themselves into small groups. The machine shop was still working at top speed. Somewhere far away the guns that were rumbling in their last desperate weeks were still demanding their full ration of iron and steel.

But when we had passed the machine shop and crossed the bridge joining the island to the mainland, we were once more in the midst of silence. The few people walking in the same direction were mostly old and crippled like Father, or else boys like me, but they soon left us behind. We moved forward like a shadow, and the farther we went the slower we moved. With every step we took I began to feel in my bones that on this morning too my hopes were going to be dashed. Father was not even strong enough to walk to the work site.

Nevertheless, we went on. We had nothing to say to each other, but we belonged together, and Father, who must have known his end was near, wanted to help me find some kind of foothold for the helpless, stumbling life I was beginning.

From the hill where at that time the town's finest elementary school stood, I happened to look back and see the church tower. The hands of the clock showed the time to be so late that work had begun everywhere. I must have sighed, for Father looked first at me and then behind him, towards the center of town as I had just done, but he said nothing. For two or three steps he tried to walk more quickly, but then lapsed into the same slow, exhausted gait.

We negotiated a second hill and made our way down into a hollow where the railway twisted about. We crossed the railroad tracks and walked on past the last houses on the outskirts of the town as it then was. Then Father stopped and sat down by the roadside against a rock. His peculiarly white face was turned away from me. He was gazing into the distance.

"The walk was a bit too much for me," he said. "But after I've had a little rest, we'll soon be there, and there's quite a lot I can do, you'll see."

The thought came to me more clearly than ever that he was

185

nearing his end, and for the first time I realized what this really meant. As he sat there he looked more like his old self, despite his pallor. His body, his hands and feet, his face, and the expression of his eyes had not greatly changed; yet one day soon he would stop breathing and be carried to his grave. A sudden dryness made my throat constrict and a vague, inexplicable terror began to hedge me in.

He had spoken in order to encourage and guide me as well as he could and to teach me to earn my own living.

But even in that he failed. When he had rested for a little while, strength seemed gradually to return to his limbs and he stood up, intending to push on. At that moment we saw a cyclist reach the top of the hill on the town side and start to descend quickly towards us. It was the municipal building contractor, who had been Father's foreman for many years. He was about to flash past us, but when Father raised his hat he looked at us more closely and stopped.

"Oh, it's you," he said. "So you're over your illness?"

"Well, I'm getting about again."

Instinctively Father tried to stand as straight as possible, and the other man was in such a hurry that he had no time to inspect him. He seemed pleased and said, "I need a good driller right now. You'll find Pajala by the workhouse crushing stone. If you get to work drilling, the others will have plenty of stone to go on with."

It did not occur to him what a second stroke and the resulting paralysis really meant, but a thought must have struck him all the same.

"If you don't feel strong enough to hold a sledge hammer, you can guide the drill. You're used to that, and Pajala's fit enough. He can swing the hammer."

"Oh, I'll be all right," Father mumbled, rather overcome, and the other man jumped quickly on to his bicycle and in a few moments was lost to sight behind a bend in the road.

He hadn't noticed me at all. I had grown so slowly during the last few years that I probably looked much younger than fourteen.

Father looked at me for a moment thoughtfully. Then he said, "Supposing I have another try, since he asked me. I'll get much better wages as a driller than the two of us together as stone crushers."

He seemed to be seized by a kind of eagerness. He wanted to return to the life that he had thought was closed to him. A feverish flush spread over his pale cheeks.

"You go back home. You can't crush stone by yourself anyway. When the foreman comes along, I'll have a word with him about you. Perhaps he can find you some easy job."

I handed him the knapsack, which he slung on his shoulder, then he nodded and moved away. It was still about a kilometer to the working site.

My mind was suddenly confused. I had not one clear thought in my head, and the forces of an inexplicable dread were churning about inside me. I stood staring after him until he disappeared behind the next bend in the road. Then I turned and ran home through the town as fast as I could.

It was a long and anxious day. Mother was working somewhere, and the younger children played out in the yard until hunger drove them in. I divided up the sandwiches and milk that Mother had left as fairly as I could; then the boys slipped outside again, and the girl, the baby, tumbled sleepily into bed. But I took no notice of them. I stayed indoors, shut myself up like a prisoner; my warden was the inexplicable fear which had gripped me in the morning.

This fear did not concern me directly, but Father. Every moment I was expecting some crushing news of him.

But no news was brought. I sat by the window for a long time staring at the tops of the trees and the clouds in the sky. Every now and then I made an attempt to do some odd jobs. I

187

went to the cellar to chop wood. I emptied the slop pail and filled the fresh water bucket. Sometimes I stood on the steps just looking at what was to be seen. But time passed very slowly. I had done my small jobs in a few minutes, and hour after hour I just waited.

Hour after hour. The anticipation of joy is never as long as the waiting for the fulfillment of fear.

From our window I could not see the road along which we had set off that morning and along which Father should return. But as I wanted to be alone and to stay indoors, I had nothing else to look at but the house and yard next door, the tops of the trees swaying above the roofs, and a speck of sky, the blue sky of late spring. Once before, I had seen all kinds of strange things up there, but now my imagination had gone to sleep. I could find nothing to look at and nothing to think about; yet I had to spend that day by the window.

Shortly before I knew Mother would come home, I lighted the fire in the stove and put the coffee pot on to heat. Then I went back to the window and stared out. When Mother opened the door, saw me, and smelled the coffee, she too suddenly grew anxious.

"Didn't you get any work?" she asked.

"No."

"What about Father? Where is he?"

"He's not home yet. He was given a job again as a driller."

Mother looked at me for longer than usual, but asked no more. When the pot boiled, she called the children in and gave us all coffee and sandwiches and then began to get supper ready. Time passed, and when it was so late that all the men from the distant working sites would have had time to get home, Mother went out and was away for about a quarter of an hour. When she came back she looked a little more hopeful.

"Markkula, who was also working at the same place, said

that Father managed to hold the drill all day," she said. "I expect it has made him so tired that he's taking longer to get home than the others."

I felt the same peculiar fear grip me again. I knew how slowly Father had walked in the morning, after a night's rest, and could imagine that the walk home would be a hundred times more taxing.

We had to wait for nearly another hour. Mother moved about getting supper ready, and my brothers and my little sister huddled in a corner of the room, whispering. Something unexplainable had seized them too; they had caught the fear from Mother and me and did not want to go outside again. I stood the whole time by the window. At this time of year the sky was still just as bright as at midday.

When supper was ready, Mother seated us at the table and went out again. The feeble hope that had burned for a short while had now flickered and gone out.

After a moment she came inside again, quite unable now to hide her anxiety. She snatched up her shawl and put it round her shoulders.

"I must go and see what has happened to him."

She hurried out, leaving the room in a silence deeper than ever.

But there was not much longer to wait. She met Father at the far side of the yard and tried to take his arm, but he would not let her. He wanted to walk all the way by himself, this last time he was ever to come home from work. When they got inside, we all left the table, and Mother began hurriedly clearing a place for Father. He glanced at the table at which he had drunk his coffee and eaten his meals for nearly twenty years, and at first it seemed as if he would sit down just as he had always done. Then his last thread of strength gave way. When he tried to hang up his hat on the peg, it fell to the floor. He stared at it in dismay; then instead of going to the table he staggered over to the bed, collapsed flat on his back, and closed his eyes.

"What's the matter?" Mother cried in distress. "Don't you want any supper? I'll bring you a cup of coffee . . ."

Father just lay with his eyes shut, and after a very long time he let out a groan.

"This was my last working day."

A faint moan of despair, a presentiment of the approaching end. Mother could find nothing to say, and we children also lapsed into silence as though sinking down into the dark. We all felt that we were surrounded not only by illness, but also by the great unknown into which we must all pass in time.

After about half an hour Father seemed to have calmed down a little. He got slowly to his feet and shuffled over to the table for his supper. When he saw us looking brighter and even a trifle more hopeful, he said, "Yes, this was the last day I'll do any work. When I left hospital the doctor said that I'd better try to get into the workhouse. So I suppose there's nothing else to do."

He said these words very quietly, completely resigned to his lot. In the mood of the moment he remembered me.

"The boy here can have his turn now at going to work in the mornings. The foreman promised him a job down by the waterfront, where they're going to start making a new street. He's to take the stoneworkers' tools to the workshop and back again."

This quiet mood didn't last long, however. Dark misery and depression attacked him several times before we went to bed. He kept quoting Jeremiah's words: "Cursed be the day wherein I was born: let not the day wherein my mother bare me be blessed."

It is not easy to go on living when your work has come to an end.

In the morning, when I ran eagerly to the place he had told

me of, another bitter disappointment awaited me. There were only four old men at work, and the foreman was as old as they were. He looked at me pityingly and shook his head.

"We're such a small gang we don't need anyone to carry tools," he said, and turned his back.

When I had gone off, full of hope, looking for a job, Father had still been in bed; but when I got home, deep in despair, he had left us once more, and he never came back.

II

Trade was so slack at that time that the marketplace was almost overgrown with weeds. A few women were put to work with knives in their hands to dig these enemies of mankind out from between the round smooth cobblestones with which the marketplace was so proudly paved. Mother was taken on among these women, but as she was now the breadwinner of a distressed family she not only dug up the weeds up by their roots, but also did some thinking. One day she said to the second foreman of the board of works, who was in charge of them:

"I have been asked by a family to go and do their washing. I wonder if my boy could take my place for a couple of days?"

This sub-foreman was a stout, florid man, and any sudden decision demanded a mental effort. He pondered for a moment before granting Mother's request.

I was allowed to go and work there. Knife in hand, I crouched among the destitute women in the middle of the marketplace, in full view of the whole town. But, after all, this time it was work.

During the first few days I dared not look about me. I worked as hard as I could, and during the short breaks I stared at the sky. White clouds were floating across the bright blue. All around me blunted knives were clinking against the cobblestones, hands crooked with rheumatism were jabbing as fast as they could, and equally twisted mouths were clacking and gossiping; but I could not bring myself either to watch or listen. I simply stared at the weeds firmly rooted between the stones, and at the clouds and the sky.

As I watched the clouds and the sky, I sometimes thought of beauty and goodness, of truth and of the war I had once waged with God and had almost forgotten.

A few days later Mother returned for a whole week to the marketplace. Then she asked the foreman again whether I might take her place for a few days. She was wanted again to do a washing.

The florid foreman waved his hand vaguely. It was difficult to gather just what he meant; but when he found me crouching in the marketplace next day he said nothing. To my relief, he pretended not to notice that a boy was squatting there instead of a woman. This encouraged Mother so much that she was away somewhere washing for four days in a row.

I tried to go on looking at the roots of the weeds that had forced their way between the cobblestones. I tried to stare at the clouds and listen to the sound of the wind, but it was no good. I was forced to see and hear other things. When the women found that I worked just as hard as they did, I became the apple of their eye. They wanted to know all about my home and how we lived, and all about the misfortunes and want that had beset us. And at secret moments of rejoicing, when the foreman was not in this part of the town, they pulled out the thermos flasks of coffee hidden in their stockings and gave me a cup too. Although at first I tried to refuse, knowing how scarce it was, they made me take it. The coffee stimulated and refreshed them, gave them strength, helped them to forget their rheumatic aches and pains for a while, and was a bond of friendship between us.

I came to know their sorrows and their defeats, and I

caught glimpses into their souls, where the fires of hope had died out long ago.

But I was made to look beyond our immediate circle as well. I saw many well-dressed people, who were not in any hurry, stop to watch us. Perhaps they wondered why the marketplace had to be weeded, and perhaps they thought it odd that a lone boy was there among the destitute, half-crippled women. That is how it seemed to me anyway, and I had to dig at the roots of the weeds harder than ever. I had to dig so fiercely that everything went black before my eyes.

Once or twice a group of boys of my own age stopped beside us.

"What are you doing here?" they asked. "This is a job for old women. Why have you been stuck among them?"

I explained that I was taking my mother's place for a few days. This was more or less true, but there was more to it than that, and they discussed my situation with almost brutal frankness. They suggested all kinds of reasons why I had been put there, and at last they asked if I was allowed to keep a few coppers for myself.

I writhed in front of them like a snake, but when they had left me, I was empty of thought or feeling. I merely existed, as I rooted out the weeds and listened to the women's talk when this was forced upon me.

Only as I watched the clouds did I remember truth and all the things I had once thought of.

Mother came to the marketplace for a week; then she gave up asking the foreman's permission and merely sent me in her place for the rest of the time this work lasted, which may have been several weeks. Perhaps she got a lot of washing to do, perhaps timber was still being loaded at the docks into the barges that went to Petersburg. At any rate, she left me in the marketplace until all the weeding was done.

For endlessly long days I sat crouched there, pulling up

weeds from between the cobblestones. During these weeks I thought of nothing and I felt nothing. It was a time of rest, or preparation for something new.

When the marketplace was weeded, I was again at loose ends, and I went several times to the labor exchange. My name was entered in a book, but the clerk remarked that I hadn't much hope of work because I was only fourteen. This man was shot a couple of years later as a Red, so it was no wonder that when I was standing in his office I began to sense what was in the air. I had not understood it when reading the papers; but when the unemployed spoke about it in our own language, I too began to have forebodings.

But it didn't really worry me any more than the war did. I wandered up and down the streets, looking vaguely for work, perhaps imagining that when the weeds had grown back in the marketplace, I would get a job pulling them out again. I dared to hope something for myself; a sleeper can sometimes open his eyes a crack.

And one day the chief foreman of the board of works, the one who had been going to give Father a job as driller in the spring, told me I could start work as a drill carrier. He had not kept his word before, but he did now, after Mother went to see him.

Suddenly I found myself with a real job, about to set out on the long road of my youth.

The same gang of men whom I had tried to join in the spring had now moved near the center of the town to build a new road. There were a lot of them now, many more than before. My job was to collect the blunted drills and crowbars twice in the morning and twice in the afternoon, carry them to the workshop, and take them back after they had been sharpened. It was not very exacting work; I had time to look about me and to think over whatever came into my mind.

It was here that I learned how steel bites into rock, how dynamite tears boulders from its side, how the boulders are put onto a sled made of planks on wooden rollers and are moved to their new position with crowbars and strong arms. Where there was an outcrop of rock, it was levelled off by removing the hump at the top, and the broken bits of stone from the top were used to fill up the hollows at the side. But it was slow work. A hand-operated drill bites slowly into rock, and boulders take time to move when there are only hands and arms to do it. The sleeper had time to think of his emptiness and to waken gradually from sleep.

The loader was a small man with red hair and a red beard, which he never shaved and never allowed to grow. Once a week he cut it with his own scissors as short as he could, and that was good enough for him. Perhaps he wanted to save money by not going to the barber, or perhaps he had no time to shave properly, for his wife was dead and in the evenings he himself fed and looked after his small children. But he was the most reliable man in the gang, and for this reason he had been made loader.

There was also a very young man whom at first I used to wonder about. All the other young men were in the machine shop, at the Petersburg metal factory, or digging trenches along the coastline. Iron was still so plentiful that large quantities of ammunition could still be made, and there was money to be had for digging trenches. Moreover, it seemed to me that any young man here should have been at least a driller. Almost anyone could be a driller during wartime if he had strong enough arms. But this young man never held anything in his hand but a crowbar. He never even took hold of a shovel.

It was not until a few days later that I found out that one of his hands had no fingers at all. There were just a couple of stumps with which he could hold a crowbar, but he was quite incapable of wielding a shovel or a drill. He had been able to hide his deformity well.

I listened avidly to every word he said, for he knew things which were not in the newspapers and which were not even spoken of in our yard. He knew where dances were held, he knew that the Russian soldiers were the Finns' rivals for the girls' favors, he knew where to go to see Russian plays and where to buy black-market liquor. He also said that we didn't have long to wait until the world we knew would change—the workers would take over, their wages would rise, and their working hours would be less. The older men looked down their noses at the girls who danced with the Russians and kept quiet about other matters, but I felt a vague uneasiness. At times I felt that I should hate both the girls and Russians, but all the same I listened to what was said about them.

I never stayed long at the working site. The blacksmith shop was a much more interesting place. When I entered the forge with my burden, I had to withdraw a little way and sit down to wait. The blacksmith would let the tools I had brought wait for at least an hour before he got to work sharpening them. He knew that it did me good to have a valid excuse for passing the time.

The peculiar thing about this smith was that he had lost his voice. When explaining something, he tried to shout as loud as he could, but all he got out was a hoarse wheeze. Otherwise he was an ordinary, small-sized man. For ten years or so he stood there behind the anvil; then he was carried to his grave and I took his place.

The blacksmith's assistant was hefty, broad-shouldered, and very young, only a few years older than I was; but in my memory he is only a shadow. The other boy, who brought stoneworkers' tools on a cart from much farther away, perhaps from outside the town, often squatted beside me in the deep

196

gloom of this huge smithy, but he has left not even a shadow behind him. I have not the vaguest recollection of his size or appearance or name. We were the only ones who were there every day, but casual callers would sometimes appear in the dazzling brightness of the doorway into our gloomy cavern. In those days a smith knew how to repair almost anything at all —fix a stoneworker's sledge hammer, a carter's axle, the fore-man's bicycle, and the broken locks of any door in town. But no shadow remains of any of these callers. Except one, and he was a very old man.

He came to the smithy very seldom, but when he did he always had a stoneworker's tools with him, just as I had, and while waiting for them to be sharpened he would sit down beside me and talk about the same thing over and over again. First of all he would refer to the strange and frightening events of the present, then he would start talking about Tolstoy. He told me that he owned all the works of Tolstoy that had been translated into Finnish. He had studied them carefully and kept referring to them when explaining the destruction that threatened the world. Sometimes he upset me just as much as Strindberg's *Isle of the Happy Ones* had done previously, and although I was still half asleep and was too tired to think about these things for very long, I had to start going to the library again in the evenings to borrow books, this time with the money I had earned myself.

Who could this man, this shadow, have been? When I gradually began to wake up and emerge into the daylight, he had vanished from my sight.

I liked being in the smithy. I didn't have to look at people or listen to what they said, I just sat in the deep gloom staring at the fire crackling in the forge, at the red glow of the iron and the sparks that flew up from the blows of the hammer against the anvil. But this was not always possible. A spirit had found its way into me which sometimes made me restless and tried to make me think, even here, of things I had once known as a child, known in the light of beauty, goodness, and truth.

III

When I once more had some new trousers and a "Sunday best" shirt, I began to feel more cheerful. I went regularly to the library and would sit in the reading room looking at the papers or in the thick air of the smoking room at the workers' institute, listening to the heated arguments of the men. When hunger really bothered me, I would go across to the canteen and order a bowl of broth. I could not afford such extravagance every day, but perhaps two or three times a week.

I was forced to wake up more and more, forced to start looking about me at reality, to prepare myself for new trials more severe than ever.

With the pocket money left over from one week's wages, I bought a leather strap, and the next week a small sheath knife, and I began to use them as I had seen other boys doing. I had seen many boys enter the canteen from the street, with their hands in their pockets in such a way that everyone could see their new knives, and walk proudly through the canteen to the smoker or the social hall. I too tried to arouse the same attention, but the very first time my pride collapsed. As I entered the smoker, two boys bigger than I was appeared beside me, and they laughed so heartily at my knife that I wanted to sink through the floor with shame.

For some reason a knife did not suit me. It made others burst out laughing in scorn. So I hid this first knife of mine, and have never since had the courage to wear one, except perhaps out in the forest.

By that time all the other boys of my age had outgrown me,

198

and perhaps it was my small size which made them laugh at my knife. Most frightening of all, however, was that my face, which had upset foremen for so long, now bared its secrets to boys as well. And they were merciless.

"I bet you've got consumption," one would say.

"There must be something wrong with your heart," said a second. "My aunt died of a bad heart and she was just as sallow as you are."

The boys in particular had no sympathy with illness. They saw a sick person of their own age as a contrast to their own good health and felt a joy that was hard to explain.

Nevertheless, I now had to seek the company of other boys and to fall back on my former acquaintances. I could not be alone now that I was waking up. One of them was at work the same as I was, but the other trudged about town hunting for a job. Desperate as his position was, however, he was better able to stand it than I had been. His face was ruddy with health and not sallow with illness. On Saturday evenings and on Sundays we would stroll about together, for reasons that had nothing to do with looking for work. We poked about the various places of amusement, we sniffed the strange smell of the Russian soldiers, and we listened to the excited giggles of the young women. We could not explain even to ourselves just what we were looking for, but we had to go into places and listen to things that were in some way repugnant to us.

I, who had listened uneasily to the talk of the young man with no fingers, could now explain all kinds of things to the other boys; I now saw them from another angle, and at the same time I grew wiser myself. When I began to understand why I must hang around the places of amusement, I also began to understand why some girls made a play for the Russians and why they were hated and despised.

One Sunday evening we met three girls of our own age who lived across the yard from me. They had collected on the wide veranda of the sauna to dance. They whirled and hopped about, two of them taking turns dancing together while the third stood alone; and each of them tried to hum a waltz or a polka. When they saw us looking at them, they started giggling.

"I suppose we'd better teach those boys to dance," one of them said loftily.

We suddenly had a violent desire to learn something, to become like those whose places of amusement we haunted yet hated. But when we felt the girls' arms around us, we grew as wooden as gateposts and couldn't learn a single step. Our dancing ended as quickly as it had begun. The girls looked at us pityingly, and when we asked stammeringly where they had learned to dance, they giggled and said nothing.

A year ago they had been the same as us. Now they had suddenly left us far behind.

That evening, however, they were willing to come with us to the movies. They had no money, but we had.

Excitedly I ran home and changed my battered shoes—I had not yet managed to buy any new ones with my savings—for Mother's, which were a trifle better. On our way to the movies we kept to the quiet side streets. Probably the girls felt shy at being seen walking along beside us boys. When we got inside, they went and sat by themselves; they were just as reluctant as we were to let anyone see that we belonged together.

But on our way home—it was late in the evening and there was not a soul about in our part of the town—the girls were anxious to be close to us. Perhaps they wanted to squeeze our hands to pay for the pictures, or perhaps at this dark and secret time of night they would have let us put our arms round them. But we were fumbling and ignorant and ashamed of our helplessness and of seeking this thing we could not understand.

Our visit to the cinema made us more cautious than ever. It had cost us our entire week's pocket money.

The girls, for their part, regarded us from then on more loftily than ever, even rather scornfully. They hardly bothered to speak to us, but they began to be seen more and more often at the various dancing places.

Once I went to the Russian theater. Years earlier I had been to see a Finnish play, but the memory of that evening had faded so completely that I could remember nothing about it. Now I had to listen to a foreign tongue and watch actors whose gestures and expressions, pain and joy, disappointments and hopes, were remote and strange.

Already the revolution could be felt in the air.

I was given a free ticket to this play. My second pal, the one who had not yet found any work, got two tickets from his mother, who in turn had been given them by a well-to-do family for whom she did the cleaning. Very few of the cultured Finns ever went to the Russian theater.

Our seats were at the front of the stalls, but we hadn't the courage to sit there among all the officers, so we went up into the gallery, which was full of ordinary Russian soldiers and a sprinkling of young Finnish workmen. I imagined that they had not come to watch the play but the women, their own Finnish girls whom the Russians were besieging, or to try and find out what was in the air. We felt safer among them than elsewhere.

This first play I saw, however, did not predict what was coming. Rather, it tried to shed light on that which was soon to be scattered, crushed, and destroyed in the storms of the revolution. I can't remember much about the play, its name or its author, but when I shut my eyes I can see vague faces and figures and I can hear the grief and joy that came from that far-off world that the Russian novels had told me about.

Next time I went to a play I bought the ticket myself. The

actors spoke Finnish, but wore Russian army uniforms and carried Russian rifles on their shoulders. They not only talked, they shouted; there was not only grief and joy, but shooting as well.

The revolution was already raging in Petersburg.

Winter had come. In my immediate surroundings, too, a stormy new season seemed to be upon us. In the smoker I heard arguments which were more heated and more outspoken than ever before. When reading the newspapers, I felt that the whole world was changing—the old world was breaking up and a new one was in the throes of being born. Even at home I heard new words, a reflection of the general upheaval. At work and in the smithy, the surging of hope and fear, joy and doubt grew more and more violent.

But even these matters made little difference to the life of the sallow-faced boy who was slowly awakening from his sleep. The most important thing was that every morning I could go to work, carry the tools to the smithy, sit for long periods in the deep gloom watching the sparks fly and listening to the clank of the metal. I was still so deep in my own darkness that not even the revolution had any effect on me.

The old men at work were just as silent, and they busied themselves with their sledge hammers and crowbars so that they would see nothing of what went on around them. Even in the smithy nothing could be heard for long stretches of time but the clank of the hammer and anvil. The greatest hope men had was to be able to open their own lunchbags at the lunch break and chew their own bread.

All the signs of unrest awoke because of other reasons. Some new personal power drove the sallow one to wander about the amusement places on Saturday evening with his pals and to listen to the strange, excited laughter of the women. Once he had been driven to the cinema with girls and twice to the theater. But this was only a surface agitation. More and more the slowly awakening one had to listen to the sounds and thoughts being born within him.

The purchase of the new trousers, shirt, belt, and the already-hidden sheath knife had only been vanity.

To me, the news in the newspapers and the new words I heard at home were merely the wind ruffling the surface of the water. In the daytime I tried to rest a little in the darkness of the old smithy, and in the evenings I escaped to the world of books, shutting the door on reality and opening other doors into the world where I did not have to live my own weary life. But I didn't often succeed in doing this. I had to wait for what lay ahead.

As I had regular work, and I suppose Mother did too, we now had something to eat every day. But poverty and misery never really loosed their grip on us. There were evenings when Mother had to go to a neighbor to beg for a tiny loan so that she could buy a few potatoes or a little rye meal. And sometimes we had to run the risk of sneaking into the forest with our sled or a sack so that we could get enough wood to make the potatoes boil. We now had one less mouth to feed than before, but the baby was growing so fast that we needed just as much food as before. A new expense was that every now and then we had to take our shoes to be mended. I tried to do what I could in the way of repairs, but I was not very good at it.

I think it was already spring when I met one of the brothers with whom I had once gone rowing to fetch wood from the island. He was working at the machine shop, like most of the boys in that family, and was full of enthusiasm. This time he did not think of his work, but of more important things.

"There has got to be a change in our working hours," he said. "We want an eight-hour day. If our demands are not met, we go on strike. Eight hours' work, eight hours' relaxation, eight hours' rest."

In our school days he had been the smallest in our class; now he was a head taller than I was. I began to wonder at all the things that were happening away above my head.

As I could not sole and heel our shoes, I had to take part of the rent money to pay the cobbler, and the landlord began to threaten us with eviction. Mother still cleaned out the drains every morning, and for that reason our rent was less than that of the other tenants; but even so we began to be in debt, frightening debt.

What could the helpless one do but flee time and again into the deep gloom of the smithy and into the still more mysterious world of books. The more I awakened out of sleep, the more desperately I had to seek ways of escape.

But these I could no longer find.

IV

I soon noticed that people were not content to speak of current events only at work, in the papers, and in the smoker. Now they collected in groups in the streets. Spurred on by the news arriving from Petersburg, they started forming organizations that gave promise of a new age. The same words that had been shouted in the theater not long before, now began to be shouted in the street as well.

The number of men earning their living at municipal work suddenly grew astonishingly large, like a mushroom in the warm rain, and wages had to be paid, not in the yard as usual, but in the street, in the same marketplace where the weeds had been plucked from between the cobblestones. But this pleasure did not last long—a mushroom's life is short. Food began to run short, even for those who had money to pay for it. The dairyfarmers, instead of bringing their milk into town, began staying at home, and anxious, complaining lines began to form in front of the few milk shops.

When the town council did nothing about it, the market-place suddenly filled with men. I did not know what it was all about. I just stood in the crowd looking at the men's faces and listening to the new tone of their voices. The town councilors were fetched from their homes at the point of a gun and marched to the council chamber. One of them was the same engineer in whose kitchen I had once stood with Mother asking for work.

Another time the men assembled in the marketplace in greater numbers, and there was talk of the armed enemy. One of these enemy soldiers had just been taken prisoner in the town. He was not shot and not kept in prison for long; perhaps he was set free or perhaps he escaped. All I can remember is that the figure of this prisoner floated above the crowd and in my mind were the old man's words about the threatening prophecies in Tolstoy's books.

The events of the autumn and winter were no longer a dream. I had to live in the midst of them and feel them in my mind and body. My own life and its inconsequential events now seemed to fade away. I was forced to see only what happened around me.

A large crowd had gathered in front of the workers' institute, among them young men with rifles on their shoulders. White and Red had already come to blows somewhere far away, perhaps at Mommila. A heated discussion was going on in one of the rooms of the institute, but the crowd in the street knew nothing of what was being said. All they saw was that a group of men had rifles on their shoulders and that they were ready to set off somewhere. These men did not know themselves where they should go, but they were burning with enthusiasm.

The Russian revolution was spreading here, the revolution

about which such inspiring songs had been sung, which in people's dreams was to wipe out all misery and give goodness and justice to everyone.

Justice above all.

Those gathered round the young men with the rifles were talking excitedly, while the crowd farther away remained silent. I stood listening to what was being said and kept craning my neck to see if I knew any of the young men with rifles. I saw some of the town's finest metalworkers, but most of the men were agitators who had been stirring up this new spirit of unrest. Some of them were driven on by good and others by evil, some by hunger and others by ideas. The ones most eager for war are always those who have been set aflame by new ideas, those who have gone to pieces mentally, or those who are as yet unawakened and want to run away from themselves.

Time dragged on, and the men were still waiting. Perhaps the men confering inside could not reach any agreement, perhaps orders were expected from Helsinki. Now and then word went round among the men that they would soon be off, but almost at once it was denied. Not yet, perhaps not until tomorrow. The rumor spread that the riflemen were to be billeted in the social hall of the workers' institute to await marching orders, but this too was unfounded. Time dragged on, heavy and hopeless.

And when the real order came at last, it was very simple, a disappointment to some, a relief to others. The rifles were to be handed back. The journey was cancelled. All the men were to return to their homes.

This time I did not run home as usual, but crept along by the dark walls of the houses, frightened and thoughtful. What was it that I had just seen and felt? I had read about the French revolution in books many times, and I had read in the newspapers and heard men talking about the Russian revolution which was then taking place. But only now did I begin to sense what it all really meant. I had seen rifles on men's shoulders and a peculiar, fierce light in their eyes.

That evening I couldn't read. I had to think, think hard, until sleep overcame me.

But next day at work I thought no more about it. The young man with the crippled hand talked about it loud and long, but the older men kept quiet as before. Casual visitors to the smithy spread exaggerated reports about the revolution, but their words were drowned in the clank of the hammer on the anvil. When I got home I had to see that the wood honestly procured was chopped or that wood was dishonestly fetched in secret from the forest, that there were enough potatoes or some rye meal for supper, and that the holes in my shoes were mended so that I could go to work next day.

I was smaller than other boys of my size, my face was yellow with heart disease or consumption, and I knew that not even books now could open and close secret doors; but sometimes I had to go with my two friends and hang round the dance halls and listen to the strange laughter of the women.

But some time later, when the Red Guardists had been formed into companies and some of them had left the town, I stood once more in the crowd of men, this time in the yard of the workers' institute. I had no idea what was being deliberated at the meeting or what kind of proclamation was made. I saw merely two kinds of faces—those weary of life and those blinded by admiration.

A makeshift rostrum had been erected in the yard, and on it climbed a so-called educated man, a man who had had good schooling; you could see this by his clothes and the expression of his face. As soon as he began to speak, a buzz of voices

could be heard from all round the rostrum: "He's drunk!"
And two or three men shouted at the tops of their voices,
"He's drunk!"

The speaker stared wildly for a moment at the hecklers.
Then he began to explain. He was not drunk; he was exhausted, on the point of collapse, for he had had no sleep for
days and nights on end. He had had to confer with Helsinki
and with the local revolutionary committee set up by the
Russian soldiers.

The man in charge of the Red Guardists who had been put
on guard duty—an athlete, a printer, a teetotaller dazzled by
the revolution—could see nothing but the fact that their lofty
and noble ideals were being sullied. He called out the guards
who were resting inside, began setting them on to the hecklers, and shouted fanatically: "Hecklers are worse than traitors! They will be shot at once!"

As the guards made their way towards the hecklers, a
strange, deep silence hung over the yard, and suddenly I
started trembling and asking myself, "They're not really going
to shoot anyone? Really shoot people here?"

All at once the speaker began to smile and he raised his
hand gently above everyone.

"You can go back, guards," he said. "These workers here
are the same kind of workers as yourselves, and you're not to
shoot each other, even if everyone doesn't always understand
what's going on."

The head of the guards was still seething with fervor. He
wanted to wipe the traitors off the face of the earth and raise
his ideals higher than ever; but the speaker's words checked
him. He had to turn the guards round and march them away,
and the meeting could begin.

This was the only Red Guardist meeting to which I was
admitted. The man on guard at the gate had not done his job
properly. He had been unable to distinguish between those

208

who were to be let in and those who were not. He had let everybody in, me included. It did not happen a second time.

But at first everyone could go and watch the last journey of the fallen revolutionaries. The first to be killed were borne through the town draped in red flags and to the sound of music. The best houses in the center of town were then strangely silent; their owners had fled or were hiding behind their doors. Inhabitants from the outskirts of the town lined the streets outside these houses, but they too were silent, as though struck dumb.

Had Father really come home for a short time or is my imagination playing me tricks? When I think back on the funeral of the first to be killed, I seem to see him standing somewhere near me. We had no more to say to each other than before, but in some way or other he was guiding my steps.

Critical weeks passed, battles were lost and won, and the fallen were no longer borne to their graves in view of the people. Food supplies dwindled, the better-class families disappeared and the chief foreman of the municipal works with them. I too sometimes had a strong desire to go with the others. Other boys of my age had joined the Red Guardists. They got good pay and were well fed. At moments of crisis soldiers had to be fed better than other people. But when I broached the subject at home, Mother began moaning with fear and somewhere behind her was Father's stern and uncompromising refusal. He wanted his family kept out of such matters, and the small flames that had flickered up inside me went out like dying embers.

During these weeks and months I had a rare advantage over others of my age: I was still in work. The factories and machine shops had come to a standstill and most of the schools had also closed their doors, but the day laborers kept on working as usual, and the hoarse blacksmith still clinked his hammer on the anvil. On a set day of the week they were paid their wages, better wages than before, in crisp new notes. The workers' institute was now full of leaders and company chiefs, Red soldiers on leave and Red women armed with rifles, so that the canteen there was shut to everyone else. But down at the docks a cellar was opened as a canteen for workers. Once a day they could get a meal there, at first meat broth and cabbage soup, later on only cabbage soup.

It was this canteen which kept me going for a long time, but what the other members of the family ate, I have no idea. This winter Mother would sometimes go across the ice to the farms on the other side of the bay and bring back flour and milk. But what the family ate for the most part and how we lived, I cannot remember.

Those who had not joined the Red Guard voluntarily were told to report one Sunday in front of the workers' institute. Father, and other invalids like him, were not summoned, but it seemed to me as if he were standing there among the others. He stood there, listening and watching, but when the others went inside, he remained outside with some old men who were no longer summoned anywhere.

All the former newspapers had disappeared at the outbreak of war and new ones had sprung up in their place. At first there had been a number of them, but gradually they dwindled to a single sheet which knew nothing about anything but its own victories. A newspaper which is an organ for those waging war must never know about anything but victories, even if there are people who doubt them. If the victories turn out to be real, the doubters must creep into their shells, must change, outwardly at least, into believers. But if there is no victory, and the sharp fangs of defeat begin to flash here and there, the flock of doubters quickly swells and spreads in all directions.

One Sunday I stopped by the corner of the workers' institute, where two young women with rifles on their shoulders were already standing, and an equally young man who had no rifle and not even the red band of the Red Guardists round his arm. It was still winter, with snow on the ground, and the men had to march across the ice between the islands. The doubter was daring and made no attempt to hide his views.

"We're losing," the young man said to the young women. "We're being beaten and we're being herded into prison camps and shot. That's what always happens to the losers in a revolution."

He smiled and gave a soft, scornful laugh. The girls ground their heels in fury and both starting talking at once, saying he was wrong and that he was committing a crime by spreading false rumors. If he didn't stop, he would be shot.

But he merely laughed. Before the war they had often danced together, so that was probably why he dared to be so outspoken.

"I'm going back to the front this evening," he said, "but I'm not going to wear a red band. It's better to be shot without it."

It had never occurred to me to wonder whether the Reds or the Whites would win the war, but now I had to start pondering this matter too. And as I was a doubter by nature, I naturally joined their ranks.

A little later, when spring was on the way, I was awakened in the middle of the night by gunfire. A single rumbling shot. Next day I heard that in the night a cannon had been dragged up on the hill near the water tower and tried out. The Red gunners didn't know their job, however, and their small cannon had burst apart the very first time it was fired.

When I climbed the hill with some other boys, we found some bright, elusive drops of mercury. The broken cannon had already been taken away.

A few days later I woke up again in the middle of the night and this time I heard the rumble of much bigger guns. The whole house shook, all the other members of the family woke up, and as the guns went off Mother let out little moans of fright. But even this firing did not last long. In the morning we heard that the coastal batteries, which had been built by the Russians on an island and had now fallen into the hands of the Reds, had tried to scare the White troops approaching the Red town, but had soon received word from the mainland that their shells were falling short of the enemy and threatening the civil population. The few White troops approaching the town did have to stop for a while on the outskirts, but this was thanks to the hastily assembled riflemen and not the gunners on the island.

Chapter Seven

I

Weary from hunger, I went once more into the smithy with two bars and some blunted drills on my shoulder and put my load down beside the forge. The smith, who was also starving now that things had come to such a pass, did not stir, but sat on by the fire, smoking canaster. I went out into the sunshine and lay down against the wall of the smithy, the thick, blackened wall of the old boiler house. It was a good spot, for the air was nice and warm and even the sand under my legs felt warm. I thought of nothing and I expected nothing. Panting with exhaustion, I merely existed.

The whole town had fallen silent. People were seldom seen about. The Reds lay low in their own homes and the Whites in theirs. Everyone was waiting for what would happen next.

Then suddenly I heard a train approaching. I should have given a start, for no trains had been running for several days, but not even this unfamiliar sound had much effect on me. I merely turned my head enough to see the train as soon as it came out of the woods, about where the station is now; at that time an abandoned sawmill stood there, and Russian soldiers had been billeted in its old buildings until quite recently. It was at that point that I saw the Whites for the first time.

The train came slowly nearer, and when at last it appeared it seemed to be crawling along like a big worm looking for safety in strange ground. The sides of the cars were protected with thick sandbags, and the soldiers sprawling behind the sandbags seemed to be all ready for battle. I wondered to myself what it could mean. Not until most of the train had rumbled past did it dawn on me what the machine guns were for. But even then I did not move; I stared at what I saw, fascinated.

When the train had disappeared in the direction of the old station, the blacksmith, his assistant, and a worker of my own age came out of the smithy. They all seemed excited.

"Now they'll occupy this town too," the smith said in his hoarse voice.

"They'll soon be beaten," the young worker said. "American-Finnish socialists have already landed in Lapland."

"Don't talk rot," the smith said. "We must keep quiet now, every one of us. And if you ask me, it's a good thing if the Whites do get into power. Then we might get some food again."

The old smith had seen more than we had and perhaps for this reason had kept silent up to now, like the other old men. They had their own thoughts.

When the smith at last sharpened the tools I had brought, I gathered them onto my shoulder and set off to take them back to work. The part of the town through which I walked seemed to be even quieter than in the morning. When I got back I found the old workmen putting their crowbars, drills, shovels, and sledge hammers away in the tool shed. Our foreman told me that I had better go home too. It had been announced by the office of works that all work was stopped for the time being.

I hurried home at a run. A knot of young men had collected in our yard. They had escaped from the front the day before or during the night, and I stopped for a moment to listen to them. They were telling each other what had happened. Their leaders had suddenly left them and everything was in a turmoil. Some had found horses and had made their way home on horseback with their equipment; others had marched mile after mile, day and night. Where could they flee? All had instinctively thought of home, where they had parents or a family. From there they had set off to war and there they returned in their hour of need.

After a moment a boy from next door, a year older than me, appeared in their midst dragging one leg. He seemed to have been wounded. His face was gray and frightened.

"What are we to do?" he asked. "The others are already handing over their rifles to the Whites and are being taken prisoner in the station yard."

The others stared at him for a moment in silence, as though considering his words and scared by them. One of the men bit his lips, then shouted: "We won't go! It's best to hide the rifles and lie low."

They dispersed to their homes. A queer silence fell over the yard. The children too were sent inside, and the doors were shut.

As I came in, Mother said that I was to stay indoors as well. She too had just come home from work and knew that all the shops had been shut. No one could say what was going to happen.

Time began to drag. Most of the time I stood by the window watching the road and the yard next door, but the few people to be seen went about their business almost at a run. Mother tried to settle down to her never-ending house-work, but every now and then she would come to the window or pop outside to listen to what was going on. My small sister and brother were sitting on the floor, unusually quiet, whis-pering things to each other which only they understood. We were all waiting for something great and momentous to hap-pen, something that was to change our world, but we could not explain to each other what it was going to be.

The night passed peacefully. In the morning I went out to the yard for a moment to listen, but there was no one there and everything was as quiet as if life in the neighborhood had stood still. Only on the road behind the yard next door did I see two people, two gray-clad soldiers with rifles on their shoulders. I knew at once what this meant, and the sight disturbed me. The men's walk was slow and unconcerned; they sucked at cigarettes in the same way as I had sometimes seen the Reds doing at their posts. During the night the rule of the defeated Reds had given way to the rule of the Whites.

When I went back inside, Mother gave us coffee and divided the last piece of bread equally among us all. She had gone to the nearby market while I was still asleep, but no milk had come and we had to have our coffee black. Mother thought for a moment, then she put the ration cards and the remaining money together and said she was going into the town to see if the shops were open and if there was any bread.

"I may also go and do some washing somewhere," she said. "I must try to get something for us to eat. Stay inside, all of you."

We started the day again by my looking out of the window and the younger ones playing quietly on the floor; but as Mother was away for many hours and nothing happened, it was more than we could do to keep still. I was the first to go out to the yard, and after a little while the others followed.

216

When we were seen from the windows, others began to appear too. We started to play, but more quietly than usual, and almost cautiously. Old men came out to sit on the steps, women to empty the slop pails and to carry fresh water and wood inside. At times it seemed that life was beginning to resume its normal course and that our forebodings had been a dream. But not for long. The next moment we saw the gray men walking along behind the neighboring yard with their rifles on their shoulders. We felt our hunger getting sharper each minute. Now and then a young man would slip off towards the town. We all knew that he and his kind had gone to give themselves up.

When Mother got home at last she had much to tell. Many more Whites had come during the evening or night. They had been stationed on different sides of the town and were moving about everywhere. Shops had been opened, but the bread ration had been halved and there was none to be had anywhere. The Reds had now been rounded up into the schools under an armed guard, and it was said that they were being taken away.

Mother told her news in the yard, and an eager group gathered round her to ask for details. Where had the Whites been stationed? What were they doing? What was going to happen now to the Reds? Would they all be shot? Mother could only shake her head.

"I know nothing. They say that some kind of tribunal has been set up, and that it will decide who is to live and who isn't. We'll know in a few days. What makes me angry is that the likes of us have all disappeared from the streets and there are nothing but capitalists and those White butchers about, and they're so happy that they're laughing out loud. Fat men are shaking hands, and the young girls are running after the Whites, and some are riding about on horseback like savages."

Outside, among the others, Mother's heart was torn by the

defeat of the Reds and the sentence that hung over them. But when we got inside, she was of quite a different mind.

"Sometimes I think it would be just as well if the Reds did get beaten. They wouldn't know how to control things, and some of them too are bad people. A lady I did some washing for said that things will gradually get better now and that even people like us will soon have enough bread."

But the view that had prevailed outside was still reflected beside the other one. After a moment she said: "It hurts me that the middle class are laughing so happily. Everyone ought to be crying now."

When she was out Mother had got our small bread ration and she divided it equally among us all, explaining that we must make it last. At the moment we had no other food.

As there was nothing special happening yet in our part of the town and as hunger was beginning to tell on us all and make us weak, we went to bed early, about six o'clock, and soon fell asleep to dream. The smallest children slept happily until morning, but about midnight Mother and I woke up. I sat up with a start. Mother gave a whimper and went quickly to the window. From the woods came the distant sound of firing. There was silence for a while, then it began again.

"Now they're shooting the Reds," Mother said, pressing her hands to her breast. "Dear God, have mercy, they're shooting the Reds."

The firing did not last long. The volleys ceased suddenly and the total silence of midnight filled the air. However hard we strained our ears, we could make out nothing more. With her hands to her heart Mother turned towards me and whispered: "Go to sleep again, go to sleep. They won't do anything to us. There are no Reds here."

She pressed me down onto the pillow, tucked me in, and crept back to bed. After a little while I did fall asleep again and had muddled, restless dreams.

In the morning I woke very early and noticed that Mother was getting dressed to go to see if there would be any milk today. I offered to go in her place. At first she told me to stay in bed, but after a moment a disturbing thought struck her and she said, "Perhaps you had better go. Children are always spared, whatever happens."

I dressed quickly, and ran to the marketplace with the milkcan in my hand. Beside the weigh-house a small group of women already stood waiting. They were all quite silent. The group got slowly bigger, and if any of the new arrivals asked if there was likely to be any milk today, a fat woman would answer each time, "We're sure to get milk now. The Whites are already in control of the town."

One or two others who also counted themselves among the Whites proudly and elatedly echoed her words. But as the Red sympathizers kept quiet, almost as though dumbfounded, the Whites soon held their peace and the wait for the milk continued in silence. No one knew what was going on in the mind of the next person.

About eight o'clock large cans of milk did arrive from the station and it was doled out without delay. I got my can filled and ran home joyfully. Mother made us the first rye porridge we had had for a long time and we ate our fill. We began to hope that things would now really begin to improve, but we were mistaken. The reason why we were so well off for the moment was that there had not yet been time to distribute the milk supplies evenly. Some of the soldiers went without any at all because of us.

Later that day I twice ran into White soldiers. In the morning I went out alone for some reason and crossed the end of the street where a detachment was patroling. When I got to the street on my way back from the woods, I stopped for a moment to see if there were any Whites about, intending to dart across the road. Suddenly I heard a strange voice to my left, and turning around I saw a White soldier sitting on a stone in the shade of a tree, his rifle resting carelessly on his knees. He gave me a friendly smile and told me to come nearer. I went up to him obediently and timidly, and he said in a quiet voice, "Couldn't you bring us some coffee? We're doing our round again in a minute, but we'll be back here in half an hour."

"We haven't got real coffee now," I answered just as quietly.

"Haven't you?" He seemed disappointed and looked at me doubtfully. After a moment he went on, "Anyone who brings us coffee will be well paid. We pay handsomely."

At that moment a man's steps were heard, and the soldier got up and went past me onto the road. When the two men met, they walked off slowly towards the town with their rifles on their shoulders. I could not quite make up my mind whether he still wanted coffee from me or not. I wondered why he had spoken to me as kindly as if I had been his equal and not his enemy.

When I got home I told Mother about it; she looked at me thoughtfully and stopped to consider this strange occurrence. At last she said, "I suppose they're human beings just like us. We have been told a lot of wrong things. Perhaps it wouldn't just have been making money if we could have given them coffee."

Some hours later, in the afternoon, the rumor went round our yard that the Whites were coming to search us. All the men who had been in the Red Guard had already given themselves up or made off somewhere, but nevertheless we were again seized by anxiety. The children were called back inside, and the women collected on the steps to talk over what was likely to happen to us. When she was down in the cellar, Mother found a rifle on the floor which had been thrown in through the window facing on the street, and she carried it into the middle of the yard, talking loudly. The owner of the rifle had evidently lived in our house, or the house next door, but no one could think who it was. Several of the women went to have a look at it and many joined eagerly in Mother's accusations. It was well known that nobody in our family had had arms. But the wives and mothers of the Red Guards tried to make out just as vehemently that their men had not had arms either. The rifle remained lying in the grass waiting for the Whites to take it away.

The women went on talking until the Whites suddenly appeared in our yard from the street. The women hurried inside and made their children keep quiet. There were three unknown gray-clad soldiers and, in front of them, riding a white horse, was a youngish tradesman formerly popular in the town. He pulled up in the middle of the yard to explain to the soldiers what the different doors were. I think he was only a guide and not an officer, but he looked so threatening on his horse that many of the housewives made a mental note of his name and vowed to themselves that they would never go to his shop, even if they were ever able to buy anything again. And this vow held good. When times changed and every shopkeeper once more had something to sell and every customer had money to buy, this man began to feel the pinch. He went bankrupt several times and kept setting up a new shop in a new place, but he was remembered everywhere and succeeded nowhere.

The soldiers searched every corner: first the rooms, then the attics and cellars, the sheds, pigsties, and privies, without finding any spoils other than the rifle which Mother had put in the yard. Nor was a single Red Guard found. It struck me that the soldiers were not very thorough. When they came into our room, they stopped in the middle of the floor, gave a glance around, listened to Mother's explanations, and broke off to look at me. I was then nearly sixteen. But when Mother hastened anxiously to assure them that I had not been in the Red Guard but had been at work the whole time, they approved of me and one of them said, "Then this lad has a good future ahead of him."

While the search was going on, the tradesman was riding round the yard, now and then shouting angrily. When the search was finished and the men had conferred for a moment, they left us and stopped some distance down the street to wait for the men who had searched the house next door to join them. Then the tradesman had to stop showing off and go after the soldiers.

When they had disappeared, there was silence in our house for a while. The families were deliberating this significant event amongst themselves. Then someone appeared in the yard, and soon others were seen—housewives at their work, old men sitting on the steps, children playing. Life began to resume its normal course. It seemed to some as if nothing remarkable had happened at all. Perhaps in the minds of one or two was the thought that life is like a dream, an idle fancy.

But in the families whose fathers or sons were prisoners there was desperate anxiety. Up to now they had been allowed to take food to their menfolk, if they had managed to find anything to eat; but word was already going round that the prisoners were being taken away from the town. No one knew where.

During the night we were again awakened by firing, and this time it lasted much longer than the previous night. The tribunal had been hard at work the day before. When silence at last returned, the night was so far advanced that Mother told me to get dressed and go again to the marketplace to see if there would be any milk. As I ran up to the milk queue I met the same cluster of women who had been there the previous morning; they were just as silent, as if struck dumb. A moment or two later I saw soldiers. There were about a dozen of them and they were on their way back to their quarters from the direction of Katariina, marching in regular lines with their rifles on their shoulders. Everyone knew where they came from, and several women looked at them for a long time, but no one said anything.

This day we got only a bottle of pasteurized milk per head. But as we still had a little rye meal left, we could have some good porridge. The bread was all finished.

During the night a large number of Red Guards had disappeared. They had been crammed into freight cars and taken away. Rumors flew about concerning the places to which they had been sent.

First thing in the morning Mother went off into town again to look for food and find out which way the wind was blowing. But after a little while she returned eagerly to say that I must go with her to the work office as at eleven o'clock they would begin paying out the back wages, and at the same time the clerk would decide who was to return to work. It seemed almost unbelievable. Why should the Whites pay out wages that had been earned while the Reds had been in control of the city? And the other clerk who had kept on working under the Reds had been arrested, so it was said. Mother had no idea what the paying out of the wages meant, but she assured me several times that the office would really be opened at eleven o'clock.

We hurried along to the office and, sure enough, found that a crowd of working women, old men and young boys had collected. The word had spread. And to our surprise, we were asked in, after having waited for a moment out in the yard. The chief clerk, whom no one had seen for the last few weeks, was standing behind a table, smiling at us. When he saw our solemn, almost scared looks, he began joking affably, "My good people, why such long faces? I'll look after you just as I've always done."

The atmosphere seemed to lighten at once. Before starting to pay out the money he made a short speech to the effect that since everything was still in a state of confusion, work was not yet in full swing, but before very long all those who were regular municipal workers and had not belonged to the Red Guard would get their former jobs back. Those whose names he called out as he paid the wages could go right back to work the next day.

This little speech and the payment of wages that immediately followed it raised our spirits still more. The women especially, but some of the old men too, brightened up and even started talking quietly. All were glad as far as I could see, and many spoke in praise of the clerk among themselves. While he had always been strict, he was also a just man, as he now proved the minute he took office again, by paying the wages and promising everyone work. But though talking eagerly, everyone kept an ear cocked for his name to be called out, and as they stepped up to the table to get their wages many felt their legs trembling with excitement. Those who were told to report to work the very next day smiled still more happily, but those who had no work offered them went off without a word.

Mother only got her wages, but I was placed among the happy few. When my name was called out and I presented myself at the clerk's table, he smiled at me more encouragingly than usual and said, "I've always looked on you as a fine lad, and as you didn't join the Red Guard like others of your age, I'll keep you in mind."

I felt my cheeks flame, and when I turned towards the others with the money in my hand I saw that many of them not only envied me, they almost hated me. Even those who were happy because of their own success and had praised the clerk, and even those who had abused the Red Guardists, felt at this moment that part of them still belonged to the

224

ranks of the defeated Red Guard, from which the clerk's words had seemed to expel me. Without a glance right or left, I hurried outside and let Mother catch up with me in the street.

But the next morning I went to work again and spent the day as usual carrying the stonemasons' tools to the smithy and back.

II

With the disappearance of all the Red Guardists who had been held prisoner, the nightly shooting ceased and even the White Guardists were seldom to be seen. Life began to quiet down somewhat, but it was still a long time before conditions became normal. The relatives of the Reds cried and mourned and kept their hatred to themselves. Although hunger gripped the whole town, they collected food from somewhere and sent parcels to their husbands and sons or took their own rations to the camps where their menfolk had been imprisoned, mostly at Tammisaari or in the neighborhood of Lahti. Thefts increased, and many potato cellars were broken into at night. Increasingly large numbers of people set off begging round the countryside. Even those who had no money could get something to eat at the farms.

These last-mentioned expeditions soon became Mother's work too this summer. At first she went twice to a village close by, from which we had previously got our milk, but the spoils were small, and as the town had no work for her yet she began to plan a long begging trip. The orphaned children of the Red Guardists and those of other destitute families were already being put together into orphanages or sent to foster families in the country, but Mother would not abandon her own. When the Salvation Army set up a small summer colony on one of the islands, she took our two smallest there, fitted herself out with two haversacks made from a bit of old cloth, took my younger brother with her, and set off on foot for the country. I stayed at home alone and was allowed to use up the others' bread rations if I could manage to buy any from the shops.

Mother and my brother were away for about a week on their first begging trip, having walked to Loviisa and beyond into the Swedish-speaking part of the country, where it was rumored that beggars did best. And they did do quite well on this trip. The Swedish-speaking district was very varied; at some farms they were driven away with shouts and abuse, at others they were asked to sit down at table, granted shelter for the night, and in the morning given more bread for their haversacks or a handful of meal for their pouch. When they got home their bundles were full of food.

But while they had been away things had become worse for me. If bread appeared in any shop, a long line instantly formed which coiled along the street like a snake until the bread gave out. And when people began to nose out in advance which shop would get food on a certain day, the unemployed would queue up before the door before dawn and stand mute or bickering in their need until the bread was doled out. It had its advantages to be unemployed. But I was at work and those at work had no time to stand in line.

For a couple of days I lived on Swede turnips which I got at a shop where a queue had already been; but when they were finished and I tried to replace them with mangelwurzels, the stomach trouble which had been bothering me for a long time got much worse. All night I writhed on the bed and only felt better after I had brought everything up. Once or twice I went to a small eating-house that had just been opened for a plate of soup made from uncleaned perch, which I could stomach better, though there was nothing in it besides the fish, not even enough salt.

By about six o'clock I had usually tumbled into bed and, as

a rule, fell into a long, but restless, sleep. Five or six times during the night I had to go to the slop pail, but as soon as I got back to bed I always fell asleep again right away.

I think it was the day before Mother returned from her first begging trip that I managed to get some real food. Before hurtling into chasms deeper than usual I was strengthened with health.

First thing in the morning I heard at work that the outer islanders had run out of salt, and as there was not even enough in the shops they had suddenly brought in huge quantities of fresh Baltic sprats for sale and begun to feed the hungry with open hands. Perhaps they also had an unusually large catch from a sea ruled by warships and fed by soldiers' corpses. During working hours I could only listen to this wonderful tale, and in the dinner hour I ran home, grabbed a basket, and hurried to the fish pier. Several big fishing-boats were moored there, many of them still half-full of sprats. The men were standing on the fish, working so that the sweat ran, heaving up the abundant catch to get it shared out. I soon noticed that some of them did not bother to count how much money was offered, but filled every vessel to the brim. If a person with fifty *penni* held out a bigger basket than the one with a mark, he got more. As there was no salt and the sun was hot, the sprats, already more than a day old, would soon have started to go bad.

Having brought my spoils home, I fetched a bucketful of cold water from the well and put the fish in it. I had no time to gut them, but had to hurry back to work. Not until the evening, when I had finished work, could I begin to clean the fish. As we had a little salt, I cleaned and rinsed the sprats well, salted them down in two large crocks, and put them in the cool cellar. I grilled a big pile of them on the coals, and having eaten my fill for the first time in months, I slept peacefully that night.

When Mother got home next day with my brother she prepared an even better meal: she fried some of the sprats and served them with real bread, and after that we had a good helping of rye-meal porridge. When we had eaten until we bulged, we were too tired to move or talk, but tumbled into bed. Life felt wonderful, big with the promise of good things. Although our bodies felt so heavy that we could hardly move, our minds, our souls, and imagination floated on high, hazily it is true and groping for vague things, but still on high, somewhere on the verge of human fancy. We were better off than we had been for a long time.

The next day was Sunday, and I did not have to go to work. Mother asked me to borrow a boat and go with my brother to see how the youngest children were getting on. Although they were being looked after by the Salvation Army, she seemed to be rather anxious and wanted to send them a little of what she had brought to cheer them up. She herself was going to see Father and take him something too, as at the workhouse they were also suffering from hunger.

We agreed with the idea at once and set off. Although our stomachs were no longer as delightfully full as on the previous evening and our spirits, instead of roaming about on high all the time, could observe the ordinary everyday world, we were in a cheerful mood when we left. As it was a nice warm day and the sea was calm, we enjoyed the row too. But as we neared the island where our brother and sister had been sent, my brother began to grow solemn. He was sitting in the stern, facing the way we were going, but as I was rowing I had my back to the island. When I noticed his uneasiness I stopped rowing for a moment and looked behind me, and suddenly I gave a start. Small children, unwashed and in rags, were lying on the low rocks of the point, on the grass by the shore and in the thicket beyond; some were moving languidly about, obviously trying to find something to eat on the

228

ground, perhaps grass, leaf mold, or bits of bark. And when some of them suddenly caught sight of us they began to wail, not shout or yell as children usually do, but wail like animals.

I glanced at my brother as though doubting what I saw. Then, grasping the oars with trembling hands, I rowed to the shore. Only then did I look at them again.

Seen from closer at hand things did not appear quite so alarming. Some of the children were still wailing, and all were dirty, but there were silent ones among them and they walked about like ordinary children. Our youngest brother clambered down from a rock and ran towards us, as did the others behind him. When I gave him the parcel Mother had sent, he snatched it greedily and began stuffing large pieces into his mouth.

"Why do you all look like this?" I asked.

"Why are they crying and wailing?" my younger brother asked in distress.

"They're ragged and dirty because nobody washes them. And we're all hungry."

"Aren't you fed at all?"

"Oh yes, sometimes, but the food's always so bad that it makes us sick. And those youngest ones are also crying because they want their mothers."

When I asked where our little sister was, he led us over to the edge of the wood, still chewing. The flock of children that had collected around us made way in silence, though the ones farther away were still whimpering. In the blueberry shrubs under the trees some of the very small children were crawling about looking for blueberry flowers. Every time they found one they put it straight into their mouths. When I took hold of my sister and pulled her to her feet, she stared at me in fright without even recognizing me.

I opened her parcel and pushed a piece of bread into her hands. She began chewing greedily, but drew back a few steps. As she ate, swallowing almost unconsciously, she stared at us from under lowered lids, half in fear, half as though trying to remember us. When she had finished the first piece, I gave her another, and this too she snatched greedily, drawing back again a little way. Only by degrees, as we talked to her and told her about home and Mother, did she begin to recollect who we were. Suddenly she began to cry in a wailing voice and finally threw herself into my arms.

"Take me home, take me home right now to Mummy," she sobbed.

The other children suddenly burst out crying more violently than ever, and they were joined by others. I looked around me in alarm. Some distance away between the trees I saw the bungalow where the children were quartered, but there was not a sign of any grownup. What was I to do? Mother had told me to leave them here, as she was setting off next week on another begging trip. My brother could only stare at our moaning sister with round, frightened eyes, and I could do nothing either except press her to me. Not until she began to quiet down and the general lamentation subsided could we too calm down a little.

Yawning chasms had suddenly opened in front of the lonely wayfarer, so that he might learn to know the basis of reality.

At last I turned to my youngest brother.

"Mummy must go off begging again in a day or two. And I have no time to stand in line for bread when I'm working every day."

"But I can wait in line all right. It's awful here and we're always hungry."

"We're hungry too, and you'd be trampled underfoot in the queue."

My youngest brother had still been chewing his bread, but now he suddenly wrapped it up as though he had remembered the days ahead and began to swallow the saliva that had collected in his mouth, looking at us warily. After a moment he made up his mind:

"If you bring us some more bread after Mummy comes home, we'll stay here for another week."

He was nine years old and could already reason.

When our sister's fit of crying was over, she collapsed in a huddle and seemed all at once to have forgotten everything except her bread. She ate it eagerly, her eyes on the ground. When I tried to explain to her that we would come back in about a week's time, she glanced at me but said nothing. My second brother and I turned suddenly towards the shore and hurried to the boat as though fleeing from something.

All the way back our consciences kept pricking us. Mother had told us to leave them here, and soon there would be no food left at home either, but we were still not sure if we had done right. Perhaps we had actually harmed them. We could not forget how dirty and ragged they were, and their despairing cries still rang in our ears.

When Mother heard what we had to tell, she sank down, weak with distress, and began to moan in almost the same way as the children on the island. She rocked back and forth in the chair and let the tears pour down her cheeks. It was even hard to make out what she said:

"Crying and whimpering . . . dirty and ragged . . . wailing like animals . . . they're being killed like the Red Guardists . . . have mercy on me, Lord!"

We could only stare at her mutely, on the point of crying ourselves. But after a while she calmed down and her face seemed to harden. She went on swaying to and fro in the chair for a moment, then she got up and swore. Many times she uttered aloud the somber, terrible curse, almost the same words as Father once used:

"Cursed be the day when I was born."

And after a moment she clenched her teeth and said, "As you didn't bring them home, they'll have to stay there another week. Tomorrow morning we're going off begging again and we'll be back by next Sunday. Perhaps they'll still be alive by then."

There would have been enough food for several days for all three of us, but Mother began to make ready for the journey. She was calmer when she had something to do. Next morning they tied up their bundles and set off on their second trip even before I went to work. Mother already knew that the farther away from town they got before dark the better shelter they would get for the night.

For me this was a week of increased bodily strength. By eking out my bread and sprats I had something to eat every day. I almost put on weight and I could save my wages. From this point of view it seemed as if things were suddenly better for us. At the end of this month we would even be able to pay our rent, which had not happened for many months. Mother's and my brother's begging trips and the placing of the two youngest with the Salvation Army were more profitable than any of Mother's earlier work.

But although I was better off physically than I had been for a long time, the experience of the previous Sunday preyed on my mind. Would the children be able to hold out until the end of the week when Mother was to bring them home? Their lives might be the price of our improved standard of living; and if they were now to die we should never be able to forget that we had saved ourselves at their expense.

The days passed somehow. While I was at work I could push them to the back of my thoughts, often for long periods. I had my own work to do, and in the smithy I could listen to the men's talk. As soon as I got home I tumbled into bed. I sought help and oblivion from self-accusation in sleep, and often I succeeded. When my stomach was full, I saw, instead of anxiety, the lights of forgiveness kindle in the chasm of despair.

Every time I was in the smithy on Saturday I kept a lookout in the direction of Hovinsaari. The only road off the island came from there and went right past the smithy. But my mother and brother were not to be seen. When I finished work I ran home, and as there was no sign of them there either I again grew anxious. I got myself some food, chopped enough wood for the whole of the following week, emptied the slop pail, filled a clean pail with fresh water, and went into the street several times to see if they were coming. As I finished work earlier on Saturdays than on other days, the afternoon seemed very long. I went to bed at the usual time, but could not get to sleep. I kept thinking of my mother, and of my brother and sister on the island. I felt that if Mother did not keep her promise now, something really awful would happen to them.

At last I fell asleep. I awoke suddenly, and it seemed at first as if I were in some strange place. The evening was so far advanced that the room was dark, a cheerful fire was blazing in the stove, and a woman and a boy were eating at the table. Slowly I began to grasp why the stove was lighted and who the two people were. As I sat up, Mother turned around to look at me and told me to come to the table.

"We've got some nice porridge now. And there's a big helping for you too."

I suddenly felt light of heart. Mother had come as she had promised. Sitting down beside them, I took a spoon and began eating with them from the same dish. Mother asked for my news, and I told her all I could remember and listened eagerly to what she had to tell of their adventures. We had a happy time together. They had brought home a lot of things this time, having been lucky enough to call at more good farms than bad; from the latter, beggars were driven away with

233

nothing but angry abuse. So the Finnish-speaking district where they had now been was the same as the Swedish-speaking one.

"Tomorrow I'll go myself and bring the children home," Mother said at last. "I must set off again next week, but the boy can stay at home this time to look after them."

In the morning she set out to row in the same boat I had borrowed the week before, still feeling hopeful. To my surprise she was away for a very long time. When at last she returned in the early afternoon, the children were not with her. She began at once to explain that conditions on the island had improved noticeably during the week. The Salvation Army had rye meal now, as well as a little milk, and the children no longer had to eat half-rotten vegetables. Moreover, the smallest ones had gradually adjusted to the strange conditions and did not cry as much as before. Mother had gone to the house where they lived, had met the women who looked after them, and talked to them for a long time. It was they who had assured her that the children were now better off.

I stared at Mother's face. What had brought about this sudden change in her? Why was she lying to me? Had the success of her begging begun to make her greedy? I had not seen it in her the previous evening, but now it seemed to have overwhelmed her. She had suddenly gotten the idea that by sacrificing her children for another week she could feed us others well and perhaps even lay in a little store of meal.

My doubting eyes made her restless. She gave me a glance and began to pace uneasily to and fro.

"What are you staring at?" she asked. "It's quite true that they're better off than a week ago. I saw with my own eyes that they had real rye bread."

When I made no answer, she burst out crying. She had to confess to herself that she had cherished in her heart a lie that gave promise of better things. The most difficult of all for her to forget was that when she was leaving, the girl had clung to her skirts crying bitterly, crying so bitterly that the sound had ripped open the wound in Mother's hardened heart.

My brother had gone out in the morning to join the other boys in the yard and he was not seen all day. But Mother and I were uneasy and could not settle down to do anything. Mother tried to get to all the housework that had accumulated during the week, but not for a moment could she forget her children left on the island. And I could do nothing but stand at the window, staring out. I stood there silent, motionless, without saying a single word. I did not want Mother to bury her pain in work. I wanted by my silence to remind her every moment that we were not to forget that day.

We must both remember every moment that for the second time the price of our full stomachs was the suffering of the two youngest ones.

And Mother did remember it the whole day. While doing her work and while eating her bread she remembered it. The later the hour, the more plaintive and guilty the words that were forced from her lips.

"Even if they do get food now, they had not been washed. Perhaps I should have brought them home after all."

"And now that I think of it, those women were not proper children's nurses. They only looked after themselves."

"What upsets me most is the way the girl cried when I left. I wonder if the child guessed something?"

Even if I had not heard these outbursts of Mother's, I could not have forgotten my sister and youngest brother. I was not forced to explain my anxiety aloud. But I was forced to remember everything, every moment.

III

After a day or two Mother set off begging again with my brother. Outwardly, this week passed quite well for me. But when the beggars arrived home on Saturday morning they had very little to show for their pains. They had again chosen a different road and had come to a part of the country where beggars were not tolerated. Because of this, the children were left on the island for yet another week or for as long as the Salvation Army would look after them. On Monday morning Mother set off alone, looking very dismal. Her traveling companion was so tired after the previous week's trip that he had been left behind to rest.

The lie of the poor was avenged.

For my brother and me this week was the severest ordeal we had yet known. The few crusts of bread brought home by my mother were all gone the very first day, and there was nothing at all left for us to eat. Queues formed in front of the shops so early in the morning, about five or six o'clock, that when we got to the queue later, after the shops had opened, there was nothing left. There was not enough bread to go round. As there was salt in the town once more, fish was to be had very seldom. For two days we satisfied our hunger with mangelwurzels and slept badly at night. On the third day, Wednesday, my brother heard that they were selling oil cake meant for cows at a cooperative store about ten miles away in the country, and went off with one of his friends to buy some. Someone had told them that this oil cake was also fit for humans. Hungry though they were, they must have covered the twenty miles quickly, for they were back almost at the same time as I got home from work. As the cakes seemed all right on the outside we baked them in the oven and ate large pieces of them. They did taste rather peculiar, but we could go to bed with full stomachs.

Not until the next day did any unpleasant symptoms make themselves felt. Nausea wormed around inside us, and we felt weaker than usual. The very sight of the deceptive oil cakes was enough, and we threw them on the rubbish heap. My

236

brother stayed in bed all day, but I had to go to work, of course, though my body sweated the whole time in a queer way and my legs wobbled as I walked to the smithy and back with the load of tools on my shoulder. Fortunately, sleep overcame us that night too, carrying us into troubled worlds of darkness for ten hours. Still, we were better off asleep than awake.

When morning came again, my brother's stomach emptied and life seemed bearable to him once more. In the bread line that day, Friday, he managed to get so close to the door of the shop that when it was opened he at last got our bread rations for the week. But my stomachache got worse and worse. The nausea stopped, but I had sharper pains than ever in the lower part of my stomach, perhaps in the bowels. Half blind and sweating all over, I staggered to the smithy and back with my load four times, just as usual, but by this time I hardly knew what I was doing. During the rests I tried to lie down by the wall of the smithy, but keeping still made the pain even worse. After only a few minutes I had to force myself to my feet and walk to and fro behind the smithy, bent double, until the tools I had brought were ready and I moved off again with the load on my shoulder. It seemed to stun me and relieve the torment.

That day was like a nightmare. I got through my work, but all I could think of was the terrible pain tearing at my body. When I reached home in the evening I tried to eat the bread my brother had bought, but I could not face it. I undressed and crawled into bed like a dying animal. But even that was denied me. The pains grew so violent that I cried out and had to struggle to my feet, wet with sweat, and walk about doubled over. As I had no load on my shoulder, only twisting my body and walking about could bring relief.

That night I was put through the hardest school of my life. I remembered neither the *Isle of the Happy Ones* nor Tolstoy's prophecies, neither right nor wrong. During the worst moments of pain there were forced from unknown depths of my soul the words of Jeremiah with which I had once battled: "He giveth his cheek to him that smiteth him: he is filled full with reproach."

My brother had been out when I got home, but he came in as my first cries of pain were beginning and stopped in alarm. He wanted to rush off and get help from one of the neighbors, but for some reason I forbade him. I wanted to be alone, away from people and their advice, alone with my pain. I shouted and shrieked my refusal so threateningly that my brother drew back into a corner of the room in terror and stared at me as though out of his wits. Twisted and bent, I carried on my desperate walking. I pressed both hands to my stomach and in between wiped the sweat off my forehead. From my mouth a continual groaning jerked out, the senseless groaning of pain. I walked and walked, back and forth, back and forth, going round the rocking chair like a prisoner in a dungeon.

"He hath led me, and brought me into darkness, but not into light."

"Surely against me is he turned; he turneth his hand against me all the day."

"My flesh and my skin hath he made old; he hath broken my bones."

When I managed to say these words from the Bible, they seemed to help.

Time and again, when I was exhausted, I lay down on the floor; there too I kept on moving. I crawled and rolled, crawling like a slug, rolling like a dog whose back is broken. I banged my head on the floorboards, I clutched at the cracks with my nails, and now and then I tried to seize something with my teeth. I could blunt the edge of the pain that was slashing at me by punishing other parts of my body.

While walking around I had forgotten my brother's presence, but when crawling on the floor I kept seeing his eyes. At some moment he had crept into bed, but he did not dare to sleep. He stared at me, dumb, stricken, gripped by terror. At such moments it consoled me slightly to see someone else suffering. But those moments never lasted for long. After a few seconds I had to start moving faster than before. I often had to stand up and let the words pour from my mouth.

"Also when I cry and shout, he shutteth out my prayer."

It was far into the small hours before the pain eased off a little. My pace slowed down, now and again I could stop for a moment, and I heard myself groaning. The sweat dried on my body. I no longer had to stand up if something threatened to stir inside me. I began to move forward again and press my abdomen as hard as possible against the floor. It helped; the drops of sweat that had just welled out on my forehead dried again, and in my ears I heard my weary panting.

By this time I suppose my brother had dropped off to sleep, and at last I too began to nod for a few minutes at a time. I had no more strength to think, to hope, or to feel, except in snatches. Exhaustion defeated pain; the torturer allowed a moment's respite.

The clock on the wall had struck every hour as usual, but I heard nothing until it struck seven. It woke me suddenly from my stupor; I should have been at work by seven o'clock. When I stood up, the pain tore again at my insides, but if I crouched and moved gingerly, it stopped. I went to the water pail and drank two cups of water. When I saw that my brother was asleep, I crept out and went to work as quickly as I possibly could. I was more than half an hour late, but no one said anything to me.

As I got the load of tools onto my shoulder and my stupor began to wear off, I felt that a change was about to take place inside me. I still walked slowly and fearfully and I did not yet dare to straighten up, but the sweat of anguish no longer oozed from my pores. I hid from the others behind the smithy, but I did not have to keep moving any more. The change that had taken place in me was even more clearly apparent from the very fact that it was best for me now to keep still. The wrenching pain rent my body only when I had to start carrying the sharpened tools back to the working site.

It felt as if hot, heavy stones had collected somewhere in the lower part of my bowels. Carrying these was much easier work than carrying the pain. My thoughts still seemed to be asleep, but even in sleep they dared to breed a hope, though as yet this had no name. Now too my spirit remembered only Jeremiah's words:

"He hath inclosed my ways with hewn stone, he hath made my paths crooked."

When work was over, I started to creep home through the wood, when release suddenly came upon me. The hot stones at the bottom of my abdomen began to burn and to move violently about. My eyes went black. I tottered blindly off the path and jagged cries of pain were forced from my lips. I squatted down, and my bowels began to empty as though my flesh were being torn with sharp bits of glass. But it was soon over. As I collapsed full length on the ground, every muscle was quivering and sweat covered my whole body, streamed into my eyes, my ears, and my mouth in rivulets, and all at once I felt a great relief. I was free from pain and from the terrifying burden. I could straighten my body, and there was only a gentle ache in my bowels. I shut my eyes, intending to sleep in peace once more.

I lay panting heavily for a while, but gradually my breathing steadied down and as it did my thoughts began to clear. I realized that I could hardly stay sleeping in the woods. I got slowly to my knees and then to my feet. As I buttoned my trousers I noticed that I was bleeding, and although the sweat had dried by now I felt something warm trickling down

240

between my legs. I cleaned myself up as well as I could with some grass, covered over my secret, and dragged myself home.

On the way, the feeling overcame me that not only had I won the struggle waged for my body, but at the same time an inner struggle which had lasted for years was also finished. Peace had been granted to me, at least for the time being. Whatever happened to me now and whatever lay ahead, I would suffer it without question, trying only to understand the inner meaning of it.

When I got home, I found Mother and the brother and sister from the island. That morning Mother had walked only a short distance and was home by midday, and the Salvation Army had brought their charges to the mainland in the early afternoon. The smell of real grain filled our room, the smell of barely roasting in the oven. Mother was busy at the stove, and the children were sitting importantly in their chairs and answering her questions. Even the youngest of us, our only sister, was taking part gravely in the conversation. Perhaps she felt a little shy; she had been away from home for a whole month, and since I had seen her last she had greatly changed. She seemed to have grown spiritually. Her words were no longer mere babble; her suffering had helped to place the simple rudiments of thought under her thin fair hair.

He whose stomach had been emptied questioned nothing at home either. He already saw everything quite plainly. He knew that he had now gained a short respite and the strength to face new trials. So he had often thought before too; the difference now was that he would accept everything in store for him calmly and peacefully.

I was calm and peaceful, but my arrival horrified the others.

"Dear God, have mercy!" my mother cried. "Have you hurt

yourself? Your trousers are all over blood. Why are you so white?"

Lying down full length on the floor, I shut my eyes and asked her to heat some water and wash the lower part of my body. I felt that the bleeding was already stopping. Young flesh, even when tortured, quickly heals. For about half an hour I was fussed over, and then told to go to bed. Mother insisted on my having some barley porridge, but I had no appetite for food yet. Sleep, which had enticed me for so long, snatched me along its fairest road, where neither joy nor sorrow can follow.

The next day was Sunday. I stayed in bed. Occasionally I would eat a little, then sink back into oblivion. There my strength grew and my wound healed.

On Monday morning I went back to work and Mother went off again on her wanderings. But the world all around us had changed. No longer was there only darkness; there was light as well. I could walk erect again just like everybody else and in the smithy I could sit in the dark and listen to the clanking of the hammer and the anvil. Our family was together, and this week we began to get our bread rations regularly.

IV

One day when I got home from work, Mother had just returned from a begging tour lasting more than a week and was just loosening her haversack, with the smallest ones standing hungry beside her. The haversack was full of pieces of bread, some dry and dirty looking, others freshly baked, and she had other things besides—potatoes, rye meal, a piece of unleavened bread, and coffee made of roasted barley. Despite her good haul, she was very tired, having walked more than twenty-five miles that day. She therefore asked me to take coffee and bread to Father.

Had I really not been to see Father all this time? I do not know. To this day my memory is a blank on this point. Not until a day or two before his death did Father step out of his obscurity for a moment.

There were two workhouses in those days. One had really been built as such on the outskirts of the town; the other was near the harbor in the small, tumbledown living quarters of a former glassworks. It was in this latter place that Father lived with other old men who had lost their strength.

When I got there, I found a group of men sitting outside enjoying the cool of the summer's evening. Father was sitting among them, but when he saw me coming he got up and took a few steps towards me. We could not say a word to each other. I held out the bottle of coffee and the other things I had brought; he took them and went to sit down in the doorway of the nearby woodshed. There he could keep his things to himself, and he drank his barley coffee in silence and ate some of the bread.

I stood a few steps away, looking at him out of the corner of my eye. His skin had taken on a peculiar look, almost the color of earth; air and sunlight no longer touched him. His moustache and hair had turned gray-white, his head shook the whole time, and he had greater difficulty than ever in using his paralyzed arm and leg. In some odd way he seemed a complete stranger to me. I was nearly sixteen and was earning my living; he was already far along the road leading away from life to some place whose end we can only divine.

When he had finished, Father wrapped up what was left of the bread and put it into his shirt. He handed the bottle back to me and got laboriously to his feet.

"How are things at home?" he asked, gazing towards the harbor. Shipping was still standing idle. There were only few sailing vessels and two or three tugs and barges to be seen.

"Mother came home today from a begging trip," I said. "They got a lot of good bread."

He looked at me and seemed pleased.

"And what about your younger brother? What's he doing nowadays? He must be a sturdy lad."

"Yes, for his age. He's been away begging too."

"He's always been sturdy. Your mother had a bad time bringing him into the world."

After this we fell silent again. It was difficult to find anything to say to each other. Father turned again to gaze towards the harbor, and his head was shaking worse than ever. A sad feeling was stirring inside me.

After a moment a stout woman appeared in the door of the house and said something to the old men sitting in the sun. They got stiffly to their feet and shuffled inside. Father turned back to me.

"We go to bed early here," he said. "I must go in too."

Raising his trembling hand, he laid it on my head just as my grandmother once did and slowly stroked my hair.

"You'll soon be quite the man. And the others have good stuff in them too."

They were his last words to me. We looked at each other squarely, just as though we understood one another better than words could say. Then he turned and began to move towards the door, dragging his right leg. I stood still, watching him until he got to the door, but he did not turn around.

Two or three days later, word was brought to Mother that Father was dead. He had had a fourth stroke in the night and not even the other men sleeping in the same room knew about it. No one could say whether it had been a struggle for him or whether he had crossed the border in his sleep.

Mother went to see him by herself and would not allow me

to come with her. When she got home she was grave but calm and told me that they had promised at the workhouse to give him a coffin and have him buried the very next day. The workmen would not do the work on a Sunday unless they got paid extra.

When she saw me staring at her in amazement, her eyes filled with tears and she went on in distress, "I've no money. And you don't get your wages until after Sunday. And with these few pence I must get the youngest ones something to eat. They are the living."

That night I slept badly again, and as I tossed and turned I heard that Mother could not get to sleep either but lay sighing and sobbing quietly. Even the peace gained by what I had been through threatened to waver in the night's darkness. My thoughts hovered round the blackest memories of the past. Whenever I tried to peer into the future, it too looked as black as the night. I felt that the same fate as Father's awaited me, and I made up my mind that I could never have children. This family's curse must end with me.

But when day dawned I regained my peace and I repeated to myself the words: "It is good for a man that he bear the yoke in his youth."

I went to work, and intended to go home at midday and follow Father to the grave. But just before the dinner hour Mother came to where I worked. She was crying bitterly. As she could neither afford a cab to the new cemetery for the pastor nor pay his fee until after I got my wages, he could not be bothered coming to read the burial service over Father that day. He would not do it until Sunday, when others would be brought to the cemetery, the deceased members of families who could afford the pastor's fee.

Had it been night at that moment perhaps my peace would have been shattered again, but it was day and I saw everything clearly. If the yoke placed on my neck began to feel heavy, I repeated the words, "He sitteth alone and keepeth silence, because he hath borne it upon him."

I had to learn that those rejected by society are even buried apart from the others. It was no use my taking time off from work. The best thing was for Mother to accompany the body to the grave alone with the driver.

In the brightness of day my peace merely grew stronger. To happy people it may seem the frozen peace of death, but without it, such as I cannot live.

Not until Sunday, when the corpse had already been under ground for many days, did the whole family go to the new cemetery. Not a single friend or relative of Father came with us. There were two other funerals, followed by a group of people. The pastor scattered the first shovelfuls of sand over the coffins and read the burial service before they were covered over with earth. We watched from a distance, standing by our own grave, silent but not beaten. The day was cloudy and so bleak that everyone felt cold, but we kept still until the pastor came to us too. He did his office for Father quickly and went back to the others.

When the pastor joined in the mourners' singing at the next grave, I thought as I filled in Father's grave:

"And thou, son of man, be not afraid of them, neither be afraid of their words, though briers and thorns be with thee, and thou dost dwell among scorpions: be not afraid of their words, nor be dismayed at their looks, though they be a rebellious house."

v

Towards the end of this summer I was moved to a new job —pulling down some ramshackle old buildings, clearing away the dismal remnants of war, and working for a time outside the town with a small gang which was beginning to straighten the main road into the town. I lost touch for a long time with the smithy and its mysterious gloom. I had to spend every moment of my working day in the bright sunlight; I watched the clouds and heard the voice of all the winds in my ears and felt their sharp bite on my cheeks.

I had to see, feel, and in my own way understand what happened in real life.

Father's grave was in a corner of the new cemetery, in a part which had not yet been put in order. Not even when they were dead could those spewed out by the community be placed beside or even near the others. A month or two later, in the autumn, when things were a little better for us, Mother got a carpenter to make a cross and went off to erect it on Father's grave. When she got there she could not find the humble mound on which she had strewn her few flowers. Over Father's body ran a wide, new road. The municipal gardener in charge, embarrassed by Mother's questions, tried to make out that Mother was mistaken and that Father's grave was under the rubbish heap beside the road. Mother made no answer; sobbing quietly, she smoothed the rubbish heap and put up the cross in the hope that the toes of the body lying beneath the road would reach it.

When I saw Mother's tears that evening and heard what she had gone through that day, I spent another night tossing and sweating. It was just about the time of my sixteenth birthday. But when a new day dawned, a cold calm filled my heart once more. I did not hate the town. Without it we could not have existed. This town was our only source of livelihood. And such a thing one cannot hate. But it was from me that a reminder must come that the town also had its dark side, and I said to myself, "Do not let the rich and happy forget the poor and miserable."

I did not hate the town, but often I felt that the town hated me.

As individuals, all were kind to me. I was treated well at work and as I wandered about in the evening I met both Whites and Reds, who told me about themselves so openly and candidly that I often fancied the Whites took me for a White and the Reds for a Red. Only I myself knew who I was. I began going again to the reading room and the public library as often as I could. I studied the newspapers of all parties and I chose my books with care.

They let me exist. They gave me work and food. I felt my muscles and brain growing strong. But the town hated me and wanted to obliterate every sign that showed where I had come from.

After a few years even our cross was destroyed. The graves of respectable people began suddenly to extend towards Father's cross; when they reached it, the despised man's grave was blotted out once and for all. A well-made mound and a dignified tombstone capable of resisting time were put in its place.

That year even the graves of the defeated Red Guardists began to flourish outside the cemetery; our grave was not allowed to be anywhere but in our own hearts.

There it was and there it is still. As long as we live it will remind us of its existence, and the black shadow it throws will accompany the deeds of even the best people.

VI

I knew the town well. I knew many things about the State, too. I had seen with my own eyes how it had been born of hopes and disappointments, agony and blood, honor and shame. For the first time it was breathing freely with its own lungs and thinking with its own brain. I had read in the papers the kind of pain that still racked it, the kind of mis-

248

takes it made, and how, in spite of all, it grew stronger and more stable and began to stand on its own feet. But my small light did not then reach outside the town. I was unable to know whether the State meant anything to me before it touched me.

The year before Father's grave was obliterated, our independent State—the State which belonged to us all, victors and vanquished alike—in the process of developing and getting rich bought the town's largest cellulose works, which had been in the hands of foreigners. In order to provide tolerable living quarters for its workers, many of whom had only recently returned home from the prison camps, it also bought up a lot of dwelling-houses, including the block in which we lived. At first an attempt was made to evict all those who did not work in the factory, but it failed. The law protected those who had paid their rent. Hands were laid only on those who were in debt to the landlord, as we were.

I did not hate the State either. Perhaps it was not even aware that people like me existed. It only wanted to get rid of us for the same reason that rubbish was cleared off the streets, so that people could breathe properly and look around contentedly. But we too wanted to live, wanted, wanted . . .

One day the police carried our belongings into the yard. Other equally unfortunate families soon found someplace else to live, but we stayed in the yard for a whole week. The town had arranged housing in the former Russian barracks and schools, but Mother tried desperately to find a room of our own. We spent the nights in a tent of sacking and had our meals in the middle of the yard in full view of everyone. We had food by then.

Those evenings I did not go anywhere. In the daytime I was at work, but the evenings I spent in the sack tent, thinking. I had to keep remembering these words:

"Judge not, that ye be not judged. For with what judgment ye judge, ye shall be judged: and with what measure ye mete, it shall be measured to you again."

I had seen that hatred breeds hatred and that two wrongs never make a right. I had seen victors and vanquished, and I had also seen that they could not do without each other. Not even the State set up by the victors could start its factory without the defeated. And in my own body I had been made to know that suffering is not subdued by hatred. On the contrary, it grows still greater.

There in our sack tent, I realized that hatred is the first thing you must teach people to destroy.

At last we were taken to an old building, right next door to the workhouse in which Father had died, which the Russians had used as a barracks during the war. We were put in the same room as two other families, two families whose fathers had lost their lives in the birth-pangs of our State.

In that room, amongst three families, I began unaided to practice the art of writing

I blamed nobody. An unfortunate could not be one of those who hated or blamed. By way of a reminder, he would try to note down what had really happened, what the people around him had thought, hoped, and done, and what the consequences had been. He fancied, too, that if he were to find the true cause of manmade misery and grief, perhaps he could pass on this light to others and help it to shine where darkness reigned.